MW00638522

— THE — ENVIRONMENTAL ENTREPRENEUR

Where to Find the Profit in Saving the Earth

JOHN THOMPSON

LONGSTREET PRESS
Atlanta, Georgia

Published by
LONGSTREET PRESS, INC.
2140 Newmarket Parkway
Suite 118
Marietta, Georgia 30067

Printed in the United States of America

1st printing, 1992

Library of Congress Catalog Number 91-78059

ISBN 1-56352-003-6

This book was printed by Book Press, Inc., Brattleboro, VT.
The text was set in Palatino.
Cover illustration by Shelley Lowell.

To
Tyler, Dakotah,
Garland,
and
the world's other
babies.

May life on Earth
be sweet for you
at fifty.

CONTENTS

Part One
THE PROBLEM

CHAPTER ONE

COLLECTIVE MYOPIA

A new economy rises
over a sleepy human village

If the environmental problem is to be solved, the business
community will be left to solve it. Unfortunately, the business community is generally unconvinced that a real problem exists, and there is certainly no economic incentive to
turn around the machinery of commerce and industry to con-
front it. Serious environmentalists understand the consequences of environmental degradation but offer few acceptable solutions to the problem and generally lack the wherewithal for corrective action. At grave risk between these oppos-
ing camps lies the cause of the problem — the public, you
and I and our kind, who are neither environmentalists
nor entrepreneurs but drive world economies with our
purchases and votes.

Ecology and business must come together, and we the public must make it happen. That, then, is what this book is all
about: getting the public environmentally savvy enough to
force changes in the conduct of business and turning the "good
ship enterprise" away from the rocks of ecological disaster.
How to start? First, we have to believe that there is a
problem of sufficient magnitude to warrant the massive com-

mitment to correcting it. Then it would help if we saw the profit in the problem.

In all great problems there are great opportunities. Solve man's problems, fill his needs and desires, and a market is born. Supply the demands of the market and riches flow. In this basic maxim of human enterprise lies the solution to the problem: enlightened self-interest and the desire for wealth are the very cornerstones of the free-enterprise system that has propelled man to unimaginable heights; perhaps they can be harnessed to head off an unimaginable fall.

So what is the environmental problem? How big is it really? What's to be believed in the plethora of environmental information rained into our midst? Let's see . . . then let's leap ahead to the critical next phase in the environmental movement — solutions and the opportunities they present. Let's look at the possible, bold solutions that can cut deeply into the environmental problem and produce extraordinary profit in the process. Neighborhood recycling programs are important, but altogether they won't make a blip on the pattern of environmental degradation locked in on planet earth. The problem is big, the solutions must measure up; the opportunities are commensurate with the challenge.

Look carefully at the human condition, and you can see in the environmental arena all the elements that spawned the enduring fortunes of the last hundred years — Rockefeller and Getty in oil, Carnegie and Morgan in steel, the du Ponts in chemicals, Eastman in photography, the Watsons in computers. "Human activities are affecting the Earth as a whole now, and the best estimates at the moment are that the effects will become profound over the next decades," said George Woodwell, director of the Woods Hole Research Center, in 1986. The U.S. Department of Energy recently noted in a report on the greenhouse effect that "Human effects on atmospheric composition and the size and operation of the terrestrial ecosystems may yet overwhelm the life support system crafted in nature over billions of years." It is not to the indices of GNP, interest rates, or stock prices that one should look for the keys to the future but to the "biological product," explains Lester Brown of the Worldwatch Institute. "This is what's shaping civilization. It is changes in the photosynthetic product that determine ultimately how many of us the earth can support and at what level of consumption."

Oblivious to where it is, mankind stands at the threshold of unprecedented change. The aggregate and scope of earth's environmental degradation and mankind's arrogance in the face of it virtually assure a whole new set of rules for the conduct of business in the foreseeable future. Change the rules and the game changes — that's the opening long exploited by the enterprising. Those who anticipate and successfully adjust to change reap the rewards, frequently profiting tremendously in the process. It has always been so. That's the good news. The bad news is this: not only may there come a collapse of the economic gridwork on which modern business is conducted, thereby rendering traditional enterprise passé, but the human species — tomorrow's entrepreneurs included — may not survive the coming ecological disaster to capitalize on the exciting opportunities it presents. Doomsayer! you say. Banish such thinking from the podium and from the mainstream of modern, "can-do" economic practice. John Naisbitt, respected author and futurist, will tell you that such lamentations are ridiculous. In *Megatrends 2000*, he looks ten years into the future and sees a booming global economy with happy consequences all around. Oh, there will be troubling environmental problems, he concedes, but "a growing global consensus that we all must work on the environment together" will somehow correct the situation. "The doomsayers in our midst hate to hear that economic good times are just around the corner, so sure are they that the United States and the world are going to hell in a handbasket," he writes.

Few business leaders today are so bold as Naisbitt in their public denunciation of the environmental factor in future economic trends, but the ranks of naysayers are formidable. Can smart, decent people like these be wrong? Yes. Decidedly yes. Don't listen to them. These people want proof, and nothing short of the sky falling will do. Because it hasn't fallen after years of screaming that it is, the naysayers turn a deaf ear to the rattles and groans of crumbling supports and shifting foundations. All the while, it's business as usual. Protection of the status quo by those who benefit the most from it is an old human story. Economist/curmudgeon John Kenneth Galbraith calls it the "convenient social virtue." "Ethical judgments have a strong tendency to conform to what citizens of influence find it agreeable to believe," he explains.

The captains of industry, past and present, capitalist, socialist, communist, or otherwise, have inadvertently shepherded the consenting, rapacious masses to the very threshold of self-annihilation. Traditional supply-and-demand, consume-and-discard enterprise is killing us, period. Say it. Believe it. It's true and it is absolutely essential that the public understand. For the villain is us. We the public are the markets for the goods and services of business and government. It is we who consume the immeasurable volume of material provided by our benefactors. It is we who excrete the consumption in unfathomable depths. It is we who leach the earth of life and decimate humanity from the impoverished bottom up. Fred Smith, Jr., president of the Competitive Enterprise Institute, a Washington, D.C.-based public interest group, notes: "Current policy assigns virtually no responsibility for pollution to the individual. He's viewed as the helpless victim of a willful technology implemented by an immoral market system." That, of course, is incorrect. Business simply supplies the demands of the customer. We the public drive the economy. It's time we learned where it is going and how it is fueled.

There is no higher form of self-interest than the breath of life. Cost/benefit analyses that fail to take into account the basics of human survival are going to look pretty silly twenty-five years from now if the simple act of breathing "fresh air" shortens the life of mankind; if massive climatic changes, habitat degradation and/or rising waters force mass exoduses of once stable population centers; if no amount of money can buy a healthy walk in a real woods on a clear, beautiful day or a long, natural life for our children. What would people pay for naturally occurring fresh air if none were available? What would be the cost of potable water if its availability were restricted to pure life-support status? The value of another new road or development or product is going to pale when the covering of one more square mile of land or the destruction of one more ecosystem or the discharge of one more supertanker of burned fossil fuel tips some ecological balance the wrong way once and for all. Given the benefits of an environment that sustains human life now, what cost is too great to ensure its survival? Nowhere does it say that the free-enterprise system has to destroy earth. The system can function whatever way consumers and the electorate and enlightened self-interest dictate.

Public perceptions of the environmental problem, only newly formulated, are misfocused and therefore dangerous. The public is presented with pieces of the problem, not the whole problem; people see the consequences of environmental degradation falling on animals, plants, and other things rather than on themselves. The sheer volume of media coverage and environmental product claims convinces them that this problem too shall pass. For all their invaluable work, organizations like Greenpeace, the Sierra Club, the Wilderness Society, the Audubon Society, and others probably got the public off on the wrong foot with their focus on specific environmental issues — elephants, whales, eagles, snail darters, Three Mile Island, old-growth forest, Love Canal, the ozone hole, the Aral Sea, the *Exxon Valdez*, soil erosion, air pollution, acid rain, and other real and unsettling problems.

Furthermore, environmental rhetoric, strident in the woolly-hippie days of the 1960s, was toned down in the seventies and eighties to be more acceptable in the mainstream. The strategy worked — all of present-day environmental awareness we owe to the environmentalists; but in becoming acceptable, the rhetoric has become too soft; too many real and present dangers are now veiled in understatement and obfuscation. Isn't a "sustainable society" that is not sustainable simply unsustainable? Does that not mean we die? The talk is about saving the environment. If it isn't saved, doesn't that mean that man has no place to live and thus must cease to be? The media, government and big business speak the same way because they learned the language from the environmentalists.

Thus is the public presented with fragmented, disconnected,

doom-and-gloom scattershots around the central figure in the issue — man. It's as if whales and elephants and condors can't survive in this singular environment but mankind can. Why can mankind live and other air-breathing, water-requiring, food-consuming, territorial living things can't? The answer is that mankind can't. Mankind cannot survive in a closed environment that, one way or another, kills off wholesale other species that share the same life-support system. The biosphere of earth is a single, contiguous entity. Tear it here, poison it there, and you tear or poison the whole. Cripple the natural mechanisms that maintain an environment suitable for human existence and you get a different environment. Mankind's best scientists won't be able to see the effects of these problems until looking back on them — after they are in place. Too late.

Mankind is killing itself. You are not going to hear it from the media or government or big business. Journalistic responsibility dictates against alarmist reporting; political expediency requires evenhandedness; cash flow says you don't shut down the machinery that feeds you. It's OK to say that wild elephants are perishing or the protective ozone layer is being destroyed, but it is not acceptable to say that man is at risk — grave, imminent risk.

The popular press, so important in shaping public opinion, does not understand the environmental problem. Environmental reporting for the general audience is new. Because scientists and academicians defined the problems and first raised the alarm, the environmental arena seems scientific and technical. There never have been many effective scientific/technical writers for the masses; public demand just doesn't warrant it. So it is that we learn of environmental problems in fits and snatches as the media chases one trendy story after another, never seeming to grasp that each is a part of a bigger story. A good example is a curious succession of articles that appeared in *Newsweek* magazine between March 19 and April 30, 1990, coinciding with Earth Day 1990. Robert J. Samuelson, a respected journalist, began the series with a column entitled "The Way We Diaper," a slap at those who protest the use of disposable diapers. "Disposable diapers are an instructive metaphor for the exaggerations of modern environmentalism," he wrote. "The tendency these days is to call many different problems 'environmental' as if the label — all by itself — implies an impending catastrophe whose solution is a moral imperative. . . . 'Environmentalism' thus becomes a loose collection of diverse concerns, with few distinctions made about whether some problems are more serious than others."

The switchboard lit up at *Newsweek*, and "Letters To The Editor" the following week flayed Samuelson for his gaffes. One reader pointed out that a third of the 18 million disposable diapers discarded annually contain raw, untreated sewage that can contaminate ground water and pose health threats. In a comparison of the environmental virtues of disposable diapers versus cloth diapers, Samuelson factored in the energy consumed in washing and delivering cloth diapers but overlooked the energy, trees, petroleum, and chemicals that go into the production and delivery of disposable diapers. Another reader wrote that 1.3 million tons of wood pulp and 82,000 metric tons of petroleum-based plastic are used to make disposable diapers every year. Comforted by the statistic that the average American throws away only slightly more garbage today than he did in 1970, Samuelson was reminded that the population has grown some since then; that, in fact, forty million more tons of garbage were generated in 1986 than in 1970.

On April 16, Samuelson was back with "Diapers: The Sequel — Environmental Problems Are More Complicated Than the Good Guys vs. the Bad Guys." Yes, "the doodoo had hit the fan," he acknowledged, and he sought to clarify himself. "Every environmental problem is not a tragedy," he wrote. "Landfills don't take up much room and no one sees them anyway. . . . Once filled, dumps are usually landscaped so they're not eyesores. . . . There's no evidence that [disposable diaper] feces threatens public health by contaminating ground water. . . . Medical wastes in landfills pose almost no risk. . . . New landfills prevent ground water pollution by being lined with both plastic and impermeable clays [and] drainage pipes at the bottom catch any water so it can be recovered and treated. . . . The letters reacting to my [previous] column reflect widespread ignorance, because the facts are either wrong or out of context. . . . What my critics really resent is that I've denied their moral superiority. . . . Our [environmental] rules and actions need to be grounded in common sense and accurate information. We need to grasp the ambiguities and conflicts. Good intentions aren't enough, and exaggeration and misinformation can have perverse results. Just because you think you are doing good doesn't mean that you are."

Newsweek elected to run no letters to the editor the week after this column appeared. The assault must have been horrific. Proving yet again that arrogance and a little knowledge are a miserable marriage, Samuelson jumped from the pan with his first column into the fire with his second. Nothing he wrote was accurate in the real world of garbage disposal. More important, he missed completely the basic tenet of waste disposal and, indeed, of life on earth — you can't throw anything away. The biosphere is a closed system; virtually no earthly matter, whether solid, liquid, or gas, leaves the envelope. Throwing away waste is a delusion. All the garbage ever created is still with us in one form or another. Most of it has long since converted to that whence it came, dust unto dust; some remains as accumulated debris, more and more of it antithetical to human life.

The industry of man threw more than 4.5 billion pounds of waste pollutants into the atmosphere in 1987 alone, including 235 million pounds of known cancer-causing chemicals, according to a recent announcement by the U.S. Environmental Protection Agency.

Human excrement thrown raw onto the ground in Mexico City dries, becomes airborne, and comes back to the populace as "fecal snow." You don't have to drink the water in Mexico City to get Montezuma's Revenge; breathing is sufficient.

Winds across Russia's Karachay Lake, the most polluted spot on the planet, mist the surface waters and blow across the land radiation doses two and a half times greater than those emitted by the Chernobyl nuclear accident in 1986.

All the nuclear waste ever created is still with us, stored in vats in nuclear plants or subterranean nooks and crevices around the world. All the PCBs and dioxins, some of the most poisonous substances on earth, are still out there on plant floors, back lots, and dumps of one sort or another. Billions of gallons of toxic chemicals, sixty percent of the hazardous waste generated in the U.S. prior to 1986, has been "disposed of" by injecting it through deep wells as much as 1,500 feet into the earth. But it comes back — as a huge "toxic blob" on the floor of the St. Clair River north of Detroit; as bubbling, noxious leakage in Vickery, Ohio, and Erie, Pennsylvania; as poisonous additions to the drinking water of Beaumont, Texas, and Belle Glade, Florida. . . .

Burning waste, burying it, encapsulating it, injecting it, or sinking it succeeds in little more than hiding it from view. It's still with us, and it swells from incalculable points around the globe. Throw a banana peel on the ground, and it becomes part of the humus; dump modern man's refuse into mountainous piles, and it becomes lethal concentrations of dyes, inks, acids, oils, heavy metals, and other corrosives and toxins that escape into the air, run off into coastal estuaries and bathing areas, leach into the soil and ground water, and overwhelm sewage treatment plants. The cadmium and mercury of a single flashlight battery are no threat tossed into an open field. Vast numbers of flashlight batteries deposited in a landfill begin to concentrate the poisons. Incinerate the garbage, a common practice that reduces the volume of debris by as much as eighty percent, and the cadmium and mercury are pooled. Multiply this scenario by the scores of other harmful elements times a world of dumps, and the threat of waste disposal becomes more apparent.

Newsweek would have done well to continue the tit-for-tat between Samuelson and his readers; it's good journalism and instructive. But the magazine seemed to opt for cutting its losses. Meg Greenfield, in an April 30 column, tried to strike a note of compromise: "All sides in the environmental debate have a credibility problem," she wrote in a piece entitled "The Word's Too Big" (Environment is the word that's too big for her; "overblown terminology," she called it). She put herself — and by implication, her associate Samuelson — in the category of layman and acknowledged that "most of us don't have a clue" about the scientific questions concerning the environment.

It is not just the media that grope along in their leadership role. Science wallows dispassionately in narrow specialties that give rise to study after study but fails miserably to make the connections that convey fully the environmental reality. Laws are promulgated to solve this environmental problem and that, gradually proliferating into a maze of compromised bureaucracy that wearies voters and accomplishes too little too late. Educators teach environmentalism from the biology department instead of the business school. Industry stalls and spars, losing ground here, gaining it back there — fiddling while the city burns.

The immediate danger in the reconstitution of earth's environment is ignorance. People, headed by those who inform and lead us, are still defining their terms, studying the issues, debating still whether there really is a critical environmental problem. Hard, irrefutable facts abound, but they are obscured in a cacophony of charges and denials and muddled in one long, obligatory study after another. I interviewed four leading electric utility scientists on the subject of acid rain in 1979. I knew that acid rain was real — even then there were too many dead lakes and rivers, too many damaged forests, monuments, and buildings, and too much leached soil to deny its existence; and I knew that power companies were a leading contributor to the problem. The scientists knew that acid rain was real and that indeed their employer was a contributor to the problem; they also knew that acid rain would be a major environmental issue of the 1980s. The corporate/scientific conclusion that emerged from that two-hour interview was . . . "The issue needed more study."

Unsaid, but tacitly understood by all in attendance, was

that the longer the acid rain problem could be relegated to the back burner of "further study" the longer the electric power industry — and every other fossil fuel-burning operation — could put off correcting the problem. No need to spend good money on something that's legally not broke. Enough of the media and government accept the "further study" conclusions of industry that the tactic still pays dividends in the 1990s. Technologies that can reduce acid rain-causing sulfur emissions from burnt fossil fuels are still not required and, consequently, there is no real start on solving the problem.

The biosphere raises its warning flags but people misconstrue. Missed is the recognition that each environmental problem is the mark of a larger beast tearing at the delicate fabric in which we all are sheltered. Every injury to the environment that supports life on earth is a jab at . . . our children. You and I seem to be bearing up, but the hammer falls on our children — not generations off in the distant future but today's toddlers and their children.

So don't be swayed by environmental scoffers who would continue essentially as before. Mankind can perish. It is not necessary for the world to "blow up" for man no longer to be able to live here. A change here, an alteration there, and the aggregate of it all coalesces into a different environment in which some species adapt, some don't. It's the nature of things. Extinction has claimed ninety-nine percent of all species that ever lived, reports the National Geographic Society in a June 1989 article by assistant editor Rick Gore. The fossil record reveals at least twelve mass extinctions of animals on earth over the last 800 million years. The die-off of the dinosaurs, the extinction best known to the general public, also took sixty to eighty percent of all other animal species with it. The latest die-off began 11,000 years ago and continues today, scientists believe. The first animal species to go were the biggest: mastodons, mammoths, saber-toothed cats, huge ground sloths, short face bears and dire wolves. Today, what remain of earth's largest creatures near elimination, but the injury goes deep into animal life at every level and size. The common thread in these extinctions over the last 11,000 years is man: man the hunter, man the exploiter, man the enterprising.

Beware the naive who think the environmental problem is now recognized and being solved. As proponents of California's ambitious "Big Green" environmental legislation learned on election day 1990, rhetorical support doesn't necessarily translate to political and economic action. And environmental advertising claims are as much new packaging of old products and services as real corrective action. The media blitz leading up to Earth Day 1990 rekindled a low fire under much of the public; some recycling and other "easy" environmental programs will become popular and effective, but the hard stuff will come slowly if at all.

When 28,000 timber-related jobs go on the scale opposite the old-growth forests and spotted owls of the Pacific Northwest, the trees and the owls are going to go. When lack of refrigeration is the main cause of food spoilage in developing nations, don't look for them to abandon the production of chlorofluorocarbons (CFCs) just because earth's ozone layer is in trouble. When Middle East oil flow to America and the rest of the industrialized world is threatened, untapped oil fields beneath pristine wilderness areas and in-close marine environments will feel the bite of the drill bit; renewed cries will go up for nuclear power.

What will become of environmental action when the public finds its mobility threatened by the imposition of fossil fuel taxes and other assessments to reduce private car usage? How will the relatively affluent of the industrialized nations respond to the reallocation of some of their wealth to support the hundreds of millions of hopelessly poor who tear down the rain forests, strip the steep slopes of trees, and overgraze marginal land to eke out another day of sustenance? The atmospheric buildup of carbon dioxide, the most voluminous of the greenhouse gases, could be stabilized (not reduced) at current levels if emissions worldwide were cut to 1950 levels, a reduction of sixty to eighty percent. Is there anyone who believes that will happen short of an ecological disaster? When farmers and ranchers in the western United States are required to pay for the real price of water, when the consumer is faced with paying the depletion cost of natural resources that go into his goods and services, the test of man's environmental resolve will begin in earnest. What is the value of the twenty-four billion tons of topsoil lost in agricultural use every year?

The Iraqi invasion of Kuwait in August 1990 laid bare a hard fact of life: no real transition away from fossil fuel dependency had occurred in the seventeen years since the Arab oil embargo of 1973. You can't turn around environmental problems overnight, particularly when you never get started.

Make no mistake: the environmental effort is barely out of the theory/computer modeling phase; little real action is under way that will curb environmental degradation generally, none that will halt it.

Be alert for the "ecologically blind" who simply miss the yawning chasm. With too little grasp of ecological reality, economists, industrialists, and politicians project conditions well into the twenty-first century as if they will be but linear extensions of today; more of the same, just better.

Think for yourself. Get knowledgeable about the environmental problem. Draw your own conclusions. When the view you enjoyed in your town twenty years ago is now obscured by air pollution, know that other views in hundreds of towns across America and thousands around the world are similarly clouded. Know that from outer space a visible pall of pollution shrouds the planet that was not there when astronauts first took in the breathtaking view nearly thirty years ago. No, it's not just the air in your town that's polluted; it's not just your forests, land, and waters that are degraded.

Individuals, the silent majority acting in its own behalf, is going to have to save the species *Homo sapiens sapiens*. Governments are not going to protect us without inexorable pressure from the public. Traditional business and its traditional leaders can't be expected to change so long as the public continues to buy what they sell. Environmentalists can carry the battle for the rest of us just so long. Free enterprise and hard-core self-interest perhaps can head off environmental disaster. Perhaps.

CHAPTER TWO

OBFUSCATION

What exactly is the environmental problem anyway?

Let's look at the whole of the environmental problem with the focus on man rather than animals, plants, things, or places.

Man as presently formulated has certain basic requirements to live in large numbers: sufficient air to breathe of a very specific, unalterable composition; water to drink that falls into narrow parameters of purity; food to eat that provides specific nutrition in specific volumes; and space to live sustainably. In this context, man faces real and present danger in the breadth and diversity of environmental degradation and the corresponding increase in world population. As the life-support capabilities of the planet go downhill, the demands on these capabilities go up. Somewhere the lines will cross. Mankind whistles through the graveyard in the belief that the lines won't cross or that they will cross so far out in the future that the present is the wrong time to deal with it. This mentality fails to take into account the potential of the many environmental changes, known and unknown, to coalesce in unexpected, relatively rapid, irreversible ways. Chlorofluorocarbons (CFCs) have wafted into the upper atmosphere since the 1930s; nothing seemed to happen until 1985 when, over a single winter, the massive ozone hole opened over the Antarctic continent. Then another hole begin to develop over the Arctic region in 1988. All of a sudden, mankind faces a major ecological threat that could be with us for another 150 years if the production of CFCs ceased immediately. The consequences? We'll just have to wait and see.

Now that the problem is with us, scientists from the National Center for Atmospheric Research in Boulder, Colorado, warn that a major volcanic eruption could touch off a catastrophic worldwide ozone loss . . . and that there is nothing we can do about it. "We can only hope that such an eruption does not occur," said physicist Guy F. Brasseur in the spring of 1991. Not long after the words were out of his mouth Mount Pinatubo in the Philippines erupted, spewing high-altitude clouds of gases, ash, and debris around the planet. At least twice as powerful as the Mexican El Chicon eruption in 1982 that destroyed ten percent of the ozone layer in the Northern Hemisphere, Mount Pinatubo is just the sort of natural event Brasseur warned about. The effects on the planet's ozone level should be evident sometime in the summer of 1992, he reports.

The Soviet Union (now the Commonwealth of Independent States) began in 1954 to divert water from the Aral Sea to irrigate cotton fields in the nation's southern republics. By 1964, this important body of water, the second largest in Asia, began to suffer; not long afterward, it collapsed. By 1989, the Aral Sea had lost forty percent of its surface area and two-thirds of its water, a volume one and a half times that of Lake Erie. Never in recorded history has such a large body of water disappeared in the time span of a single generation. "Up to a point the environment could cope with irrigation and the [Aral Sea] remained reasonably stable. But then a threshold was crossed, and suddenly the effects became enormous," explained Philip Micklin, an authority on Soviet water management and a geography professor at Western Michigan University.

For a hundred years, developers and planners reshaped the natural ecosystems and watershed of south Florida. Prosperity reigned on what engineers called a "hydrological masterpiece of natural and artificial systems that held back swamp and sea." In the 1980s the hydrological masterpiece began to fall apart. Booming demand from five million people pulls down the delicate freshwater aquifers that nourish the region, salt water pushes in to fill the void, rising sea levels threaten to overwhelm the elaborate pumping and drainage system that currently maintains the integrity of the area's precious water supply. Pollutants from agriculture, industry, and landfills seep through the porous limestone rock to further compound the problems. Much of south Florida's farmland, rich organic muck from the drained Florida Everglades, decomposes when exposed to air and disappears — one inch per year, five feet since 1924. The intricate food web of the Florida Everglades, eons old, could collapse and die in less than two decades.

Timbuktu, founded on the edge of the Sahara Desert in 1100 A.D., remained an improbable garden of green up to the early 1970s; today it is a desert with no future. One-fifth of the world's topsoil, a finite commodity more precious than oil, has been lost to mankind since 1950; atmospheric carbon dioxide, principal contributor to the greenhouse effect, increased twenty-five percent between 1958 and 1988. The burning oil fields of Kuwait added another twenty percent to worldwide emissions of carbon dioxide, sulfur dioxide, and nitrogen oxide. Not for 35,000 years did man reach the 100 million population mark; it now takes about thirteen months to churn out the same numbers.

"What nature used to do in several thousand years man is doing in twenty," said Monique Mainquet, deputy director of the U.N. Desertification Control Program. Acid rain, greenhouse heating, hazardous waste, nuclear waste, garbage disposal, ground water contamination, deforestation, air pollution, soil erosion, human overpopulation — all this is occurring in the same test tube at the same time. All these maladies and others we don't yet know about are born of the same parent; none is a condition unrelated to the others. All play a part in the reconstituting of the environment of planet earth, home-in-a-bottle to you and me. So what's brewing in here? No one really knows, but the size of the container is not as big as you might think.

For mankind, the world is not so large as it seems. The earth's total surface area exceeds 197 million square miles. With 5.3 billion people on earth, that's .0371 square miles per person, about 23.7 acres. Man does not and cannot live on all the earth, however. Let's subtract from the total of earth's surface those areas where man doesn't live. First, the oceans, seas, lakes, rivers, and other bodies of water cover more than 140 million square miles. The Pacific Ocean alone is larger than all the land on earth. Water, then, reduces man's potential living space by better than seventy-one percent — 16.8 acres, leaving 6.9 acres per person. No populations live on the Antarctic continent or Greenland, a combined landmass the size of South America; only two million people live on the frozen lands above the Arctic Circle. There's another one-acre reduction. Warm deserts in which negligible numbers of people live cover better than twenty percent of the earth's land area. Cold deserts like the Tibetan plateau are another one-sixth of the total land area. Few people live at mountain altitudes above 10,000 feet, an area as big as the United States.

Net it out and man's world, that portion of earth on which he can live in sizable numbers, is a fraction of the planet; maybe one or two acres per person, about the size of a football field. Of course, mankind doesn't live spread out evenly across the landscape. He lives clustered on the richest parts — where the water is, and the food and fuel and tolerable temperatures. Increasingly he fills these niches to overflowing and draws down his available resources. Egypt's fifty-five million people, for example, crowd onto the less than four percent of the land that is arable, leading to a population density in the settled area of the country of 4,700 people per square mile. So what does overpopulation look like? Is it people stacked elbow to elbow in a blanket of flesh stretched off in every direction as far as the eye can see? No, it is simply too many people for the available life-supporting resources of a given locale, whatever that population figure might be.

In all his multitudes, and more on the way, mankind lives on less than ten percent of the earth's surface. That leaves a lot of open space between population concentrations. As targets for rain to hit, for example, human habitat is easy to miss. Monsoons that provide lifegiving rainfall to India missed the target in 1988. The monsoons dumped their treasure of water out in the Indian Ocean that year and India baked. Parched by several years of severe drought, large swaths of semiarid land began to fail, desertification set in. The loss of life was staggering. It's not that the monsoons didn't come, they just didn't come to the right place; same rainfall, only no people lived where the rain fell that year. Many more misses like that and key parts of India will cease to be habitable by large populations of man.

China is another easy target for rain to miss. Much of the country is desert or near-desert to begin with. Of the land that is arable, the hardworking, efficient Chinese farmer extracts the fullest measure of nourishment. But after 5,000 years of continual agricultural use, the farmland is stressed and overworked. There is little margin for error here; a major shift in rainfall deposition would be catastrophic.

Still a smaller target for rainfall is the breadbasket of the world — the central plains of the U.S. and Canada. Forty percent of the grains consumed worldwide are grown here. The Soviet Union's agricultural land is precariously concentrated amid frozen tundra, inhospitable steppes, desert, and mountains. Nearly all of humanity, in fact, is fed on a dangerously small ten percent of the earth's arable land. And this critical resource, earth's richest human habitat, shrinks every year with little hope for reversing the decline.

According to research compiled by the Worldwatch Institute, three historical trends are converging to make it more difficult to expand food output. One is the growing scarcity of new cropland and fresh water that affects most of the world. The second is the lack of any new technologies such as hybrid corn or chemical fertilizers that can dramatically boost output. And the third is the negative effects of planetary environmental degradation on food production. "Any of these trends could slow the growth in food output," says Lester Brown, senior researcher for the Worldwatch Institute. "But the consequences of all three could alter the food prospects for the nineties in a way the world is not prepared for."

Climatic changes are not just theory or remote possibilities, nor are they mere whims of nature; man alters weather patterns on a massive scale with his deforestation, overgrazing, farming practices, and other environmental manipulations. As either chicken or egg, desertification runs hand in glove with climatic changes. Renowned for its fecundity in Biblical times, for example, the Fertile Crescent today is essentially desert. The Greeks and Romans hauled logs from the dense forests of temperate Egypt. Today, except for a narrow band along the Nile River, Egypt is ninety-six percent desert.

In Sudan, the southern edge of the Sahara Desert moved south through the country eighty miles in the decade ending in 1987. The entire Sahal region, six West African nations just south of the Sahara, have essentially lost the battle against the encroaching sands. Hundreds of millions of dollars of international relief funds spent in the 1970s and 1980s to hold back the desert accomplished little. The sands roll on. In 1991, twenty-seven million people there faced starvation.

What was recently the bottom of the great Aral Sea is now 11,000 square miles of desert; salt storms swept from this exposed seabed blanket vast stretches of Soviet Central Asia where fruits and vegetables once grew in abundance. Summers in the region have gotten hotter, winters colder, the land drier.

Every year — in the Americas, Asia, Africa, and Australia — nearly fifteen million acres (23,438 square miles) of once productive soil, an area half the size of Kentucky, become unrecoverable wasteland. With nearly one-third of the earth's land area classified as arid or semiarid, the potential for further desertification is enormous. Countries like China, India, Indonesia, Israel, Japan, North and South Korea, Pakistan, and Peru already rely on irrigation rather than rainfall for more than half their domestic food production. Egypt could grow virtually no food without water drawn from the Nile or underground aquifers. California's Central Valley and the Aral Sea basin — the fruit and vegetable baskets of the United States and the Soviet Union respectively — could barely be cultivated without supplemental water supplies. Without irrigation, crop production in critical grain-growing areas of northern China, northwestern India and the western U.S. Great Plains would drop by one-third to one-half.

Irrigation is a terribly effective farming technique (a third of all crops come from the seventeen percent of farmland that is irrigated), but it is flawed. It takes fresh water to irrigate and, surprisingly, there's not a lot of it. While there is a great deal of fresh water suspended in the atmosphere, less than three percent of the planet's vast store of water is fresh; three-quarters of that is locked away in glaciers and the Antarctic ice cap. Fresh water actually available for human use in lakes, rivers, and accessible ground water amounts to only about one-third of one percent of the world's total water supply. It is from this reservoir alone that all land-bound living things, including man and croplands, draw their water. Agriculture takes the greatest part of it, approximately seventy percent. Worldwide, cropland irrigation removes 1,275 cubic miles of water annually from the earth's rivers, streams, and underground aquifers — six times the annual flow of the Mississippi River. Increasingly, the water requirements of major urban areas compete for finite supplies.

In many places the water is running out. Ground-water

levels are falling more than three feet per year in parts of the North China Plain, a vast expanse of flat, fertile farmland that yields a quarter of the nation's grain. Water tables beneath Beijing, a city of twelve million, have been dropping three to 6.5 feet per year; a third of the city's wells reportedly had gone dry by 1990. Heavy pumping in portions of the southern Indian state of Tamil Nadu reportedly dropped water levels as much as eighty to a hundred feet in a decade. Israel, Jordan, and Syria get most of their water from the Jordan River basin. In 1990, Israel used ninety-five percent of the renewable water supplies available to it. The World Bank predicted that if current consumption patterns continue, water demands in Israel, Jordan, and the West Bank will exceed all renewable supplies within six years. Jakarta, Indonesia, a teeming urban sprawl of 8.6 million people, sits nervously on a freshwater aquifer that drops several inches every year.

Drinking-water supplies in Uzbekistan and other regions adjoining the Aral Sea are not only declining but are polluted with pesticides, crippling life in many villages. Fifty percent of the drinking water in Czechoslovakia is tainted with industrial chemicals; ninety-five percent of the river water in Poland is unfit to drink; Romania's river water is undrinkable. Forty percent of Iowans drink water containing detectable quantities of pesticides. A million and a half rural Americans rely on well water tainted with excessive levels of nitrate. Four hundred thousand leaking underground storage tanks degrade U.S. water supplies.

The freshwater aquifers beneath the sands of the Outer Banks of North Carolina are sucked down every year by the incessant development above. Watering a lawn in Palm Beach County, Florida, literally contributes to the death of the

27

Everglades by depleting the water cushion needed to keep the marshes wet through the dry seasons. Atlanta, Georgia, a booming Sunbelt metropolis of 2.5 million people, draws its water from a nondescript little river that a grown man can wade across in normal times without getting his shoulders wet. Los Angeles, built on a desert, stretched its water line a hundred miles into the once prosperous and fertile Owens Valley and sucked it dry. Ancient Mona Lake was next: it has fallen forty feet since 1941, and thousands of acres of former lake bottom are left bare and exposed. For its water, Phoenix, Arizona, also robs Peter to pay Paul. In the U.S., nearly 9.9 million acres — roughly a fifth of the nation's irrigated area — are watered by pumping in excess of recharge. By the early 1980s, the depletion had become particularly severe in Texas, California, Kansas, and Nebraska, four important food-producing states. The great Oglala Aquifer that feeds much of this area falls six to twelve inches each year.

Not only is irrigation tenuous because of competing demands for finite water supplies, but the very practice of repeatedly flooding land can inadvertently create desert and wash man-made chemicals and natural elements into poisonous concentrations. The very best fresh water typically has a salt content of 200 to 500 parts per million (ppm). Drinking water in the U.S. normally carries 500 ppm of salt. (Sea water has a salinity of about 35,000 ppm.) Pouring water on land naturally leaves behind some salt after it percolates into the soil and evaporates. Two to five tons of salt will be left on a 2.5-acre parcel of land irrigated with 13,000 cubic yards of water per year, a fairly typical rate. If subsequent "washings" don't flush away this salt it can build up to enormous quantities in a couple of decades. Fertilizers, pesticides, and other chemicals accumulate the same way.

With thin water supplies becoming thinner, irrigated lands increasingly fail to receive the flushings necessary to maintain the health of the soil. Aerial views of abandoned irrigated areas in the world's dry regions show vast expanses of glistening white salt, land so destroyed it is essentially useless. Forty-three million tons of windblown salt from the dry seabed around the Aral Sea falls on croplands for hundreds of miles, turning once productive farmland into desert. In India, salinity reduces yields on some 77,200 square miles, and an additional 27,000 square miles have been abandoned as salty wasteland. China has about 27,000 square miles of saline and alkaline agricultural land, and Pakistan 12,400 square miles. In the United States salt buildup lowers crop yields on twenty-five to thirty percent of the nation's irrigated land. On and on it goes across man's habitat. Salinization may be reducing crop yields on as much as twenty-four percent of irrigated land worldwide.

Then there is the leaching effect of water. Lethal selenium concentrations have been found at twenty-two different wildlife sites in the western United States, including Kesterson National Wildlife Refuge, sometimes called the Three Mile Island of irrigated agriculture. A natural element, selenium is needed by humans and other animals in small amounts, but at greater concentrations it is highly poisonous. Irrigation washed more selenium and other dangerous chemicals out of the soil in several decades than natural rainfall would have done in centuries, states a Worldwatch Institute report.

Obviously, mankind's food cannot continue to be produced in growing amounts on diminishing resources. Nowhere on earth are there real compensating gains in topsoil, water, and the other ingredients of food production; everywhere they contract. Trend lines are crossing. The share of land planted in crops increased from the time agriculture began until 1981. Since then, the area of newly reclaimed land has been offset by that lost to degradation and conversion to non-farm use. Twenty-four billion tons of topsoil are lost worldwide to erosion or development every year. Grasslands, principal food supply for livestock, have shrunk since the mid-1970s as overgrazing slowly converts much of it to desert.

Irrigated croplands began to decline on a per capita basis after 1978. World grain output slowed during the eighties for the first time since records have been kept. With the pulsing increases in world population — an average of 84 million people per year during the eighties — grain output per person dropped seven percent between 1984 and 1990. Grain stocks were precariously low worldwide as of 1989. Surpluses amounted to little more than pipeline supplies. From this position, any fall in grain production would translate directly into hunger and starvation for much of the world's chronically poor. Five hundred million people were at risk with the approach of the 1990 growing season. Nowhere is the problem more evident than in Africa. The combination of record population growth and widespread land degradation has reduced grain production per person twenty percent since 1967. Extrapolating these trends into the future produces what analysts at the World Bank in 1989 called the "nightmare scenario."

Food consumed per person in Africa and Latin America is lower at the outset of the nineties than it was at the beginning of the eighties. After decades of gradual improvement, infant mortality — litmus test of nutritional stress — is rising in Brazil, the Dominican Republic, El Salvador, Ghana, Madagascar, Mexico, Peru, Uruguay, and Zambia. Add to this bread line of familiar faces a host of newly hungry — an unnerving portion of the 400 million residents of the old Soviet Union and communist eastern Europe, millions of starving North Koreans, even millions of down-and-out Americans. Against this backdrop of world food supplies, the question must be asked: in whose bread line would America stand if food production here plummeted for one reason or another?

Since recorded history, modern man has occupied essentially the same corners of the earth. Because his numbers were smaller, his societies more transportable, and the lead times longer, preindustrial man adapted to great environmental changes by migrating elsewhere in his limited range. The migration into Egypt of the traditional ancestors of modern Jews was caused by a famine in the "land of Canaan" in the early second millennium B.C. In 1846, hundreds of thousands of Irish migrated to the United States because poor agricultural practices left their country dependent on a single strain of potato that was destroyed by a virus in 1845-46. And in the migration dramatized in John Steinbeck's novel *The Grapes of Wrath*, thousands of American farmers were forced off their land by the economy and the environmental disintegration of the dust bowl drought.

Contrast these occurrences with recent events. Millions of Kurds trying to flee the Iraqi army in the spring of 1991 found themselves with nowhere to turn. The Turks wouldn't take them, nor would the Iranians, so they piled up in cold, barren, mountainous cesspools and began to die. The Bengalis suffer unspeakable losses of life to monsoons and other waterborne calamities because their country is essentially a giant flood plain, the seas are rising, there is too little high ground available, and there is nowhere to run. Eastern

Europeans cannot migrate from their blighted lands and must raise their children in the waste. The last Amazonian Indians have been cornered; there are no more deep forests in which to withdraw. Today's humanity — vastly larger in numbers, rooted in concrete and asphalt and infrastructure, hemmed in by physical and political obstacles — has little room to adjust, and little time in which to do it if dramatic changes occur rapidly. In these narrow confining walls, mankind tightens the screws on himself. Given his tenuous, increasingly cramped position on earth, man persists in consuming and wasting the habitat that supports him.

CHAPTER THREE

EQUIPMENT FAILURE

As goes the machinery of life on earth, so goes mankind

I vividly remember a journey back and forth across China in 1981. For days on a succession of trains from Canton in the east to Urumchi in the west I was bothered by something I couldn't explain. It finally came to me in the Gobi Desert, a vast cauldron of fist-size gray stones that paves the middle of the country: there, perfectly straight, disappearing far off in the shimmering distance, stood a row of steel power poles. Steel poles in a nation too poor and too frugal to squander a valuable commodity on a simple device to hold two strands of wire off the ground. Why not wooden poles, like in the West? I asked my savvy Chinese guide. "We don't have enough telephone-size trees," he replied with a sheepish smile. That was it. I had seen no real forests in my 2,000-mile trip west. Five thousand years of agriculture and firewood consumption has essentially deplumed China of extensive forestland.

A month later in northern India, I was again reminded of trees. At the end of a long day pounding along narrow back roads in Rajasthan, I was distracted by movement on the horizon. Curious, bobbing mounds slowly rose and fell across the gentle hills. The mounds proved to be heavy woven thickets of branches, sticks, and broken wood; beneath each mound labored a woman, child, or other beast of burden. Firewood. The bearers had left early in the morning. Not till dusk had they gathered enough fuel to return home. The sight became a familiar one to me during a 5,000-mile drive through much of the country. There too, forests are few and far between and, as in China, they are besieged. It occured to me that China and India are the third- and seventh-largest land areas on earth, respectively; and combined they have less forestland than the eastern fourth of the United States. Two billion mouths to feed and bodies to warm says there never again will be any great forests in China and India.

I know that lush, green America is no more than twenty-five percent covered in forest, and that percentage shrinks annually. It's said that 1.2 percent of the United States is designated wilderness area and only 4.3 percent could be so designated. Just thirteen percent of the country's virgin forest remains. A thousand years ago, what is now Great Britain was a sea of forest from end to end; today woodlands cover less than ten percent of the combined area of England, Scotland, Wales, and Northern Ireland.

I read of the massive deforestation of the rain forest in Brazil and neighboring nations in South and Central America, areas the size of the state of Virginia laid waste annually. Tropical rain forests in Southeast Asia are destroyed fifty percent faster than in Brazil. A third of Sumatra's woodlands disappeared between 1982 and 1990. The country, along with Thailand, Burma, Cambodia, and other nations of the region, could be stripped by 2010. El Salvador has almost no forests left. Neither does Haiti. Costa Rica was once almost completely cloaked in tropical forests, holding within its small confines perhaps five percent of all plant, animal, and insect species on earth. By 1983, after decades of explosive growth in the cattle industry, pastures covered roughly half the nation's arable land, only seventeen percent of the original forest remained, and soil erosion was rampant. Madagascar, a giant tropical island 1,000 miles long and half again as large as California, has but twenty percent of its once lush forests left. The Indian Ocean bleeds red for miles from the runoff of Madagascar's surface. Nepal's forest shrank by half during the decade of the eighties.

I read of the die-off of the Black Forest in Germany; I see the dead fir in the Great Smoky Mountains and the dead pine in the Black Hills of South Dakota and Wyoming — all enfeebled by acid rain, an insidious by-product of man's consumption. The growth rate of yellow pine, a major species covering 162,000 square miles in the southeastern United States, declined by thirty to fifty percent between 1955 and 1985 because of acid rain and other pollutants. From 1975 to 1985, the quantity of dead pine increased from nine percent of all trees to fifteen percent. Soviet foresters report a decline in tree growth rates in central Siberia over the last few decades that is remarkably similar. In eastern Germany thirty-seven percent of the trees are dying, ninety percent suffer damage from airborne pollution. Fifty percent of all forests in Czechoslovakia are dead or dying; thirty-four percent are damaged in Bulgaria.

I know that no forests grow at the earth's polar regions, in the high mountains, the deserts, in the millions of square miles of cities and suburbs and agricultural land. Forests, in fact, are relatively rare. Including open forests or savannas only partially covered with trees, forestland may cover twenty-seven percent of the earth's land area, down dramatically from the advent of agriculture and industriliazation. Real forests, deep, dense woodlands, are a much smaller area. "If there is no more forest," observed a top government official in impoverished Madagascar, "then there is no more water and no more rice." Indeed, deforestation destroys more than trees. Forests play a powerful global role in the creation of fertile humus, the transfer of energy between earth and atmosphere, the makeup of temperatures, rainfall, and other aspects of climate, the prevention of soil erosion; and they serve as the fountainhead of many great rivers and provide fuel for half the world's people. Even more important, trees, second only to the oceans, are the principal exchange mechanism that takes up carbon dioxide and other greenhouse gases and converts them to oxygen. Trees are vital in keeping the chemical concoction we call air in the proper mix for mankind to live.

I know that if major climatic changes occur, the remaining forests can't migrate and adjust as in the past — too many farms and cities and airports and people in the way, not enough time. Prior to the industrial state, forestland had the space and the geologic time to adapt gradually to slow-developing climatic changes. If a general warming made things hotter and intolerable on the equator side of the forest, new growth would spring up on the polar side where temperatures warmed. A colder climate killed off foliage closest to the poles but the loss was recovered on the more accommodating equator side. Equilibrium was maintained. No more. If climatic changes come, the forests will simply die. Nevertheless, commercial timber consumption in 1990 exceeded 1.5 billion tons, a volume that surpassed steel and plastic combined. Government studies project that U.S.

demand for paper and wood products will increase fifty percent by 2030; worldwide demand may double.

I grew up in swampland and marshes and coastal estuaries. Many times as a child in the fifties I cried to my
mother that "they were tearing down my swamp." Indeed
they were.

The Great Dismal Swamp, fabled in Thomas Moore's poem
Lake of the Dismal Swamp, has been reduced from dimensions
that rivaled the world's great wetlands to a couple hundred
square miles of struggling, tainted drainage. Choking
algae fed by massive runoffs of fertilizers and sewage tan-
gle the shallows of the great Carolina lagoons and the
Chesapeake Bay; pollutants of every imaginable sort infect
the waters that once nurtured me. Boatyards, marinas,
warehouses, subdivisions, summer homes, and trailer
parks lie heavy among the reeds, black mud banks, and dark
canals I poled not so very long ago. I like to think now that
"they" might not have torn down my swamp, and millions
of square miles of other wetlands around the world, if
they knew the role these areas play in the maintenance of
human life.

Respected scientists say that the earth can tolerate
tremendous disruption to land and sea and air and still provide a safe haven for man; but destroy the wetlands — marshes, estuaries, and muds of the shallow continental shelf —
and we flirt with doom. Tied up in the complex chemistry
that occurs solely in these environments is the mechanism
that keeps earth's atmospheric oxygen component within
the narrow range necessary for life on earth to exist. It is oxygen above all other atmospheric gases that makes life here
possible, but it is a very hazardous element. At the historically constant atmospheric level of twenty-one percent, oxy-

gen provides for ready, controlled combustion; at twenty-six percent of atmospheric gases, oxygen would spark into an uncontrolled conflagration that would consume the surface of the earth. Without the regulating effects of earth's "marsh gases," oxygen concentrations would rise inexorably in the atmosphere until any fire anywhere would bring an end to things. "Until we know much more about the earth and the role of these regions, vital or otherwise, we had much better set them outside the limits for exploitation," wrote J. E. Lovelock, progenitor of the Gaian theory that earth itself is a giant, self-regulating, self-protecting ecosystem.

So where are wetlands today? They are caught in a killing vise between rising seas on one side and human encroachment on the other. Here too, natural mechanisms are crippled. Off and on during man's history rising seas have "drowned" the ocean side of coastal estuaries but have made up the loss by creeping inland on the higher water, converting sterile shoreline to marshy chemistry. Lower the sea level, and the reverse occurs. Today, the changes come too fast; the geographic flex is gone.

Earth's mean sea level has risen a foot in the last hundred years, a period coinciding perfectly with the industrial revolution phase of human enterprise. Geologically, that's fast, very fast. The sea level changed little before that for a thousand years. It is expected to rise another foot in the next fifty years. That could roll back shorelines along the entire northeastern coast of the United States an average of two hundred feet; in some places in flattest Florida, it could be five hundred feet. Of California's 1,100 miles of exposed Pacific shoreline, eighty-six percent recedes at an average annual rate of six inches to two feet. Monterey Bay, south of San

Francisco, loses as much as five feet to fifteen feet of shore-line annually. The shores of Cape Shoalwater, Washington, about seventy miles south of Olympia, have been eroding at the rate of more than a hundred feet a year since the turn of the century. Its sparsely settled sand dunes have retreat-ed an astounding 12,000 feet — more than two miles — since 1910. Parts of Chambers County, Texas, lost nine feet of coast to Galveston Bay in one nine-month period in 1987. North Carolina's Cape Hatteras Lighthouse, built half a mile from the ocean in 1870, finds the Atlantic tearing at its foun-dations now. Built two years after the Hatteras light, the Morris Island light near Charleston, South Carolina, now sits more than a quarter-mile out to sea. For different reasons, much of the 5,000 miles of shoreline of the Great Lakes slips underwater an inch or so each year. The north Atlantic press-es in on Great Britain, West Germany, and the Netherlands. Bangkok, New Orleans, Taipei, Venice, and other large cities around the world are threatened.

Snug up to most of the world's shoreline is man with his homes, roads, cities, farms, and industry — and his excre-ment and waste. In 1990 seventy percent of the U.S. pop-ulation lived within fifty miles of the shore. The long and storied coasts of Europe fast become cementified by ram-pant development. "In the past five years, what virgin coastline was left has been disappearing at an alarming rate," said Costanza Pera, Italy's environment minister, in a 1987 interview with *Business Week* magazine. "The risk that the whole Mediterranean basin will be ringed by cement is very real," he said. Pinched between rising waters and human development, estuaries, wetlands, and the gurgling muds of the continental shelf all around the world drown, with little replenishment now possible. Much of what remains is torn out, filled in, built on, poisoned by discharges of toxic chemicals from coastal industry, or suffocated by the effects of sewage and continental runoff.

The losses are monstrous. Twenty million acres (31,200 square miles) of wetlands have been cleared and drained by man in the lower Mississippi valley, an area comparable in importance to the temperate zone of North America as the Amazon is to the tropical zone of South America, according to a leading biologist with the U.S. Fish and Wildlife Service. A million acres (1,500 square miles) of Louisiana and east Texas estuaries have disappeared under the advancing sea waters of the Gulf of Mexico since 1900. Scientists estimate that fifty square miles vanish every year, a rate that could double by 1995. Entire parishes could disappear in fifty years.

By 1987, developers in Florida had dredged and filled one-third of the state's coastal seagrass beds, vital breeding areas for fish; half the mangrove swamps were destroyed. Coral reefs along the Florida Keys are laced with traces of pesticides and metals washed from the land. Some fish have disappeared, others are deformed and diseased, and clam beds are closed for weeks at a time. Until recently, Boston Harbor, a fifty-square-mile body of water, absorbed the discharge of oil, grease, heavy metals, and acids of 6,000 factories. Fish suffer fin rot and liver tumors and cannot be eaten by man. A 1987 report said that it would be at least twelve years before Bostonians could "stick a toe" in their historically famous harbor. A century of waste disposal in the 3,200-square-mile Puget Sound — everything from sewage and toxic metals to contaminated wood preservatives, oil, and arsenic — produces cancerous fish, dead estuaries, and food-chain contaminants for people.

A 1982 study of pollutants in New York's Hudson River estimated that 182,000 pounds of lead alone washed off the shores into the waterway's ecosystems. Massive doses of mercury and PCBs were among twenty-six other toxic chemicals that found their way into the river from surrounding farms, lawns, and city streets. Striped bass fishing from New York waters, a $14.7 million industry in 1973, was banned in 1986 because the fish, which spawn in the Hudson River, were contaminated with dangerous levels of PCBs.

Billions of pounds of heavy metals and toxic chemicals are washed into the Mississippi River every year from the factories, farms, and sewers of thirty-one states. Two thousand miles from its beginnings in northern Minnesota, the Mississippi deposits its load in the Gulf of Mexico — a continent worth of chemical debris and sewage that swirls green-brown in the blue waters. Some scientists believe the entire Gulf of Mexico is in jeopardy. The nutrients alone — fertilizers and sewage — create giant dead zones in the Gulf from a process know as hypoxia. Nitrogen from the river produces a glut of algae blooms, which sink to the sea floor and decay, using up oxygen. Under certain conditions, large areas become asphyxiating baths.

In a phenomenon called "Jubilee" in fishing villages along Mobile Bay, swarms of shrimp, crabs, and deep-sea fish suddenly appear in the shallow water just off the beaches, swimming suicidally toward the shore — and the nets of the local fishermen. The creatures are simply suffocating and fleeing desperately in any direction for oxygen. Further out in the Gulf, scientists have found "extensive, severe, and long-lasting" hypoxic zones almost every year since 1985, covering areas up to 4,000 square miles.

Hypoxia and toxic sludge killed millions of fish in Long

Island Sound in 1987 and untold tonnage of smaller marine life. Dolphins suffered and died in oxygen-starved, chemically tainted waters off the coast of New Jersey and washed ashore by the hundreds. It is the same story in the Chesapeake Bay and other bodies of water along the U.S. coast. "All our coastal systems are damaged, some so badly that we can't use them anymore," acknowledged University of Maryland biologist Joseph A. Mihursky in 1987.

Mediterranean ecosystems fight a losing battle against pollution where ninety percent of the sewage generated along the coast is discharged raw into the sea. In a 1987 survey, the Bay of Naples was found to be fouled with such "incredibly high levels of raw sewage that it's on the outer limits of the imaginable," said Italian biologist Claudio Pirro. Sewage and industrial waste cripple the normal functioning of estuaries and coastal muds in the Adriatic, Aegean, Baltic, the Sea of Japan, and the Irish Sea. Irish Sea ecosystems bear the added burden of radioactive waste discharged since the 1950s from a British nuclear reprocessing plant at Sellafield on England's west coast. Greenpeace said in 1983 that Sellafield had dumped more radioactive wastes into the Irish Sea than had been disposed of in all the world's oceans combined.

The world's oceans are big, but mostly lifeless. The important part for humanity lies close to the shore, close to man. Half the biomass on earth grows in these zones; vital chemistry takes place there, and they are in trouble. "Once the conditions of the water deteriorate, it's very difficult to halt the decline," warns Gary Mayer, associate director of environmental studies for the National Sea Grant. "Poisoning the sea will inevitably poison us," said Jacques Yves Cousteau nearly fifteen years ago.

CHAPTER FOUR

ADDING INSULT TO INJURY

Things get bad, then they get worse

In modern China I saw pure sulfuric acid emissions writhe from a smokestack in Datong, a midsized industrial city in China's Shanxi Province; I saw a new steel mill set right on the bare ground in Taiyuan, unfiltered smoke and discharge running from every opening; I saw an ancient, industrious populace straining to have more, bursting to get cranking in the industrial revolution. I saw an Indian economy closed to outside goods, a nation committed to building an industrial capability all its own. I saw rampant democracy, hustling grass-roots entrepreneurs, all of it unnervingly reminiscent of America—an America gone bust.

I know that China and India are struggling to lift themselves from poverty and that they are going to increase the consumption of basic raw materials to do it, the environment be damned. Right now they don't have the money to provide for the luxuries—scrubbers for factory smokestacks, sewage plants to avoid destroying the Yangtze or the Ganges, or local power supplies to curb the need for forest fuels. I know that Eastern Europe and the Soviet Union, 400 million people strong, ancient lands lived on and consumed much like China, have the same intention. They are going to grow; their people want and deserve as much as any other people. They didn't break out of communism for nothing. They see how the West did it; now it's their turn. Consumption of the earth, and the waste that follows, is going to increase, not decrease. And still we tighten the screws. . . .

On a writing assignment to an American nuclear power plant in 1980, I was stunned to be shown a huge vat, a silo filled with water, that contained the leftovers of every ounce of nuclear fuel that had ever come into the plant. The most dangerous radioisotopes in spent nuclear fuel can kill and cripple thousands of years from now. Looking down into that quiet pool, I could not but think that a flimsy veil of water was precious little protection against the threat that lay just below the surface. There was no good place on earth to put the fuel, so it stayed in the plant.

At that time there were sixty-seven other nuclear power plants in the U.S., 243 worldwide. They all had the same problem: no place to put the dangerous by-product of nuclear power generation. So, for the most part, it remains on site. There *was* a good place to put it, industry scientists argued at the time, if only government would allow them to implement the technology. Salt mines. Store the nuclear fuel and assorted other nuclear waste in ceramic cylinders, envelop them in a coat of lead, and store the stuff in old abandoned salt mines in Louisiana and Mississippi. Salt was impervious to water, industry scientists said; it was elastic and would bend and stretch, not fracture in earthquakes.

That was the solution offered by the best minds in the business. Then one day an innocuous little lake near New Iberia, Louisiana, did a strange thing. Its placid surface began to swirl in a giant counterclockwise vortex; it picked up speed and began to tear away shoreline and trees. Houses were ripped from foundations; barges, houseboats, a tugboat, and an oil-drilling rig were swept up in a violent Homeric whirlpool. Not long afterward, Lake Peigneur, all 3.5 billion gallons of it, disappeared down a great hole in the bottom of the lake bed, the ends of barges and houseboats sticking out to mark the spot. Where did the lake go? Into one of those impervious, fail-safe salt mines that would hold nuclear waste of awesome toxicity forever. That particular mine shaft had been dug under the lake. An oil company, drilling in the lake above, punched through to the mine. Water poured through until the roof of the shaft caved in. Any nuclear cannisters in that mine would have eventually shown up somewhere in the Gulf of Mexico along with the other debris that flushed that day.

Nothing else was heard from industry scientists about "the solution" to storing nuclear waste—until recently. People's memories are short. Fossil fuel emissions become increasingly unpopular, the tenuousness of world oil supplies is exposed anew, there is a hue and cry for a national energy policy . . . a perfect opening to dust off old arguments for nuclear power. "Nuclear-generated electricity causes neither the acid rain nor greenhouse gases that coal-fired plants do," touts a March 1990 article in *Forbes* magazine. "Safe methods of storing nuclear waste have been developed and are now being used in France." That safe method? Yes, stuff it in ceramic cylinders, encase it in concrete or lead and bury it underground in impervious geological formations. No, there is nothing new in nuclear waste disposal. The old problems lie there just as before; only the silos are older now, the waste greater, the solutions just as flawed.

And what ever happened to PCB? Remember PCB, that ubiquitous chemical solvent developed by the electric utility industry to enhance power transmission, the deadliest chemical ever concocted, according to some experts? It's still around, stored/disposed of in dead, seething places *off-limits to the public*. Dioxins, chlorinated hydrocarbons, sarin, nerve gas, mustard gas, hydrogen fluoride—all stored away *off-limits to the public*. The grounds and immediate environs of the Hanford Nuclear Reservation in Washington state, 562 square miles—*off-limits to the public*. The Savannah River Plant near Aiken, South Carolina, 310 square miles—*off-limits to the public*. The security zone around the Chernobyl nuclear power plant, more than a thousand square miles—*off-limits to the public*. The Portsmouth Uranium Enrichment complex in Piketon, Ohio; Yucca Mountain, Nevada; Sellafield in Britain; Forsmark in Sweden; Lop Nur in China—*off-limits to the public*. The list is long, the loss of habitat significant.

Add it up. Man's poisons render a large portion of earth uninhabitable, and much of what land is habitable is poisoned, if not lethally. No breast in the world holds infant's milk untainted by pesticides. Pesticides were not even invented until the 1930s, yet they so permeated the biosphere that all people, all living creatures on earth, carry them in their bodies today. On a per acre basis, Americans apply more pesticides to their lawns and gardens than commercial farmers apply to their fields. As much as sixty percent of it is for purely cosmetic purposes. Fifty thousand cases of pesticide poisoning are reported every year in the U.S. Pesticides and herbicides have so poisoned large blocks of farmland along stretches of the Mississippi River and in Soviet Central Asia and elsewhere that nothing will grow and the local drinking water is contaminated.

Copper smelting in the Copper Hill region of Tennessee devastated the surrounding countryside so completely that parts of it still look like the surface of Mars, seventy years after the initial damage was done. In eastern Germany nine percent of the farmland has been ruined by pollutants and overdoses of fertilizers. The Polish government estimates that sixty percent of the food grown in the Krakow area is unfit for human consumption because of heavy metals in the soil. The nickel plants of Siberia's Kola Peninsula and the Yamel oil fields are monuments to industrial devastation. According to a leading Soviet authority, twenty percent of the country's population lives in "ecological disaster areas" and another forty percent in "ecologically unfavorable conditions."

So man's habitat is increasingly scoured and diminished. Already there are places that are losing the capacity to accommodate humanity. Mexico City and Cairo flirt with inhabitability. Mali, a nation of nearly 8 million people, is being obliterated by desertification. Madagascar, Bangladesh, Egypt, Mauritania, Haiti, Mozambique, Ethiopia, Soviet Central Asia . . . For one environmental reason or another, these and other places not far behind are failing as human habitat.

Disease and poverty follow hard on the heels of environmental degradation. Lung damage from air pollution in young people in major urban areas is "far greater" than expected, revealed a 1990 report by Dr. Russell Sherwin, professor of pathology at the University of California. Autopsies of a hundred Los Angeles-area youths—aged fourteen to twenty-five—who died in accidents or homicides showed that twenty-seven percent had suffered severe lung damage and eighty percent had lung-tissue abnormalities. If the youths had lived, most would have developed some form of lung disease in less than twenty years, said Dr. Sherwin. Another pathologist has linked big-city air pollution to the spread of lung cancer. And according to a study conducted by University of North Carolina cardiologist David S. Sheps, carbon monoxide may cause potentially fatal heart-rhythm disturbances, even at levels that occur in the air of many American cities.

The Siberian coal-mining city of Novokuznetsk, 600,000 people in size, reports lung cancer rates thirty percent higher than the average of other Soviet industrial cities. Respiratory infections and eye irritations among children are higher. Industrial dust and sulfur dioxide are blamed. Throughout Uzbekistan and especially in the Karakalpak Autonomous Republic, people are dying of throat cancer at the highest rate in the Soviet Union; infant mortality in northwest Uzbekistan is the highest in the country. Eye diseases are rampant. The cause? Salt-laden dust from the dying Aral Sea.

Mexico City raises a generation of children brain damaged by lead particles adrift in the air. Illness traceable to pollution consumes more than thirteen percent of Hungary's health budget; at least one out of seventeen Hungarian deaths stems from environmental causes. Around the German industrial center of Leipzig, life expectancy is six years shorter than the national average. Nearby in Espenhain, four out of five children develop chronic bronchitis or heart ailments by the age of seven. Children in northern Bohemia, the heart of Czechoslovakia's industrial region, are taken out of the area up to a month each year as a health measure. Even horses can't stay longer than a couple of years in the soot-blackened Romanian town of Copsa Mica. They die from polluted air if the stay is longer.

"The worst form of environmental degradation is poverty," says A. W. Clausen, former president of the World Bank. Like the dog chasing its tail, gutted human habitat begets poverty, which drives further ecological deterioration; desperate people overexploit their resource base, sacrificing the future for the present, and fall deeper into poverty. Economies collapse in the wake of environmental destruction. Societies collapse. People suffer and begin to move.

Environmental refugees—people driven from their homes not by war or repression but by destruction of their habitat—have become the single largest class of displaced persons in the world, according to Jodi Jacobson, author of a study by the Worldwatch Institute. She estimates that there are ten million people who have lost their homes because land became unproductive or uninhabitable. There were another fifteen million *traditional* refugees roaming the earth in 1989, people displaced by fear of political, racial, or religious persecution or by war or civil strife. That is a fifty percent increase in five years. How much of this displacement owes its origins to the collapse of societies with too many mouths to feed and too few resources to do it with? "The vision of tens of millions [of people] permanently displaced from their homes is a frightening prospect, one without precedent and likely to rival most past and current wars in its impact on humanity," said Jacobson. "The growing number of environmental refugees today is already a rough indication of the severity of global environmental decline."

An African problem, you say? Asian? Consider this:

pushing hard against America's southern border is a host of people from one of the most overcrowded, underemployed, polluted, deforested, eroded, and otherwise resource-depleted areas in the world. They would run to where they can live from where they can't. "For the people of the United States," said a sociologist with the Inter-American Development Bank, "this job gap in Central America and Mexico is the scariest thing I can tell you."

Habitat is the name of the game for people no less than for elephants, whales, bears, or birds. Every species must have an environmental niche in which to survive. Wildlife, like canaries in the coal mine, is man's sacrificial alarm mechanism. If the canary dies, there's poison about; if the wildlife dies, people are in trouble. At least twenty-seven species of songbirds have been declining in the southeastern U.S. for a decade or more, according to the 1989 U.S. Fish and Wildlife Service's annual North American Breeding Bird Survey.

The sweet sounds of the wood thrush, hooded warbler, yellow-throated vireo, scarlet tanager and bluebird add to the delight of any spring day. But the chorus grows dim. The wood thrush has declined forty percent in the southern Piedmont region in the last twenty years. The eastern wood pewee declined forty percent in the Southeast since 1970. The scarlet tanager and American redstart have declined ten percent between 1978 and 1988. In the same span, yellow-billed cuckoos declined thirty percent.

Migratory birds for the most part, the Southeast's songbirds suffer from deforestation in Central and South America where they winter; pesticides, uncertain food supplies, and growing predation en route cut into their numbers. And as tropical jungles give way to cattle ranches, farming, mining, and logging, the woodlands of the United States are replaced by housing developments, shopping malls and highways. "Something serious is happening," says Chuck Hunter, biologist with the U.S. Fish and Wildlife Service. "[The songbird's] decline should be a red flag that something is wrong with the environment."

Explaining one of the cataclysmic die-offs of species during the Jurassic period, a Johns Hopkins paleobiologist recently said, "The [meteor] impact was but a final insult to an already overstressed global ecosystem." A colleague added for clarification, "Things got bad, then they got worse." Is that the epitaph confronting the world's young people of 1992?

Part Two
THE OPPORTUNITY

CHAPTER FIVE

INTRODUCTION

OK, there's a big, imminent environmental problem facing mankind; so where are the opportunities, where's the money to be made in averting an ecological disaster?

The environmental arena is as broad and diverse as the environmental problem; so too are the opportunities. Enviroquest, Inc., of San Diego, California, estimated that environmental products and services were a $120 billion industry in 1989, and only a third of that business was generated by the biggest 180 companies. The action is only now heating up. Solve or hitch your wagon to the solution of any one of the major environmental problems confronting humanity, and the world will beat a path to your door, money in hand. But where do you position yourself, what do you look for? How do you start?

Some things seem obvious but may not be the opportunity they appear. Garbage disposal threatens to overwhelm every major urban area in the United States and most other consumer-driven economies of the world. Solve this problem in an ecologically effective way and wealth will surely follow. Right? Probably, but maybe just in the short term.

Long range, the booming waste disposal industry could find itself with little product if entrepreneurs seize on the opportunity to take out of circulation the packaging debris, paper, plastics, and other modern consumer materiel that created the problem in the first place. Most older people remember when there was no waste problem: the packaging industry didn't take off until after World War II; plastics and disposable glass didn't reach the mass market until the sixties; newspapers and magazines used to go into the starting of the morning fire, and household garbage went to someone's farm, into a compost pile, or the backyard refuse pit.

Opportunities abound in phasing out waste *in the beginning of the process* rather than creating industries at the end to deal with it. High-tech "bulk" grocery stores could dispense Green Giant peas from a huge, sanitized, color-coordinated hopper into reusable containers that are sterilized and sealed right on the spot. Cereals, milk, juices, and most of the other packaged goods that fill the shelves of grocery stores could be sold the same way. Cans, cartons, wrappers, boxes, bags, bottles, and other trash would become passé. And with the packaging eliminated, bulk grocery stores could deliver their product cheaper, with better profit margins.

Some opportunities that are not obvious perhaps should be. If population growth threatens to consume the resource base on which man depends, then *population management* is a legitimate opportunity for the enterprising. Practical, effective population control solutions delivered by well-organized companies should find a ready, profitable market. Unquestionably, most opportunities for riches in the environmental field have not yet been identified because the ground is little mined, the crunch is not yet on. Who would have thought that the search for a better billiard ball would pave the way for the invention of television? The unique properties of celluloid, the material that went into John Hyatt's new billiard ball in 1870, proved to be the key piece of a puzzle Thomas Edison needed to create the forerunner of cinematography. Don't be surprised to see new ventures into the environmental arena turn up dramatic solutions unimaginable at the moment. One thing is certain: the best of environmental business opportunities will come with a *new way of thinking*. Our vision is constrained at the outset of the last decade of the twentieth century; that always seems to be the case just prior to great change.

Let's begin the exploration of opportunities inherent in the coming ecological crises with some generalities:

• Saving the human species by putting it back in the cave is not going to sell and is not necessary to the task. It *is* necessary, however, that individuals curb their voracious appetite for materiel, gain a global perspective of human habitat rather than a neighborhood perspective, and acquire a pervasive sense of responsibility to future generations.

• The heart of the environmental problem is outmoded economic beliefs.

• For farsighted companies, the environment may prove to be the biggest opportunity for enterprise and invention the industrialized world has ever experienced.

• The great design, packaging, and marketing skills that drive so much of consumer demand must be fully employed in the pursuit of riches in the environmental field.

• All major new entrepreneurial forays into the environmental field must proceed on footing prepared by communication and law: *communication* to sell the public on the value of the venture, *law* to provide the regulatory environment for change.

• The environmental field is ripe for the creation of corporate conglomerates—major businesses forged from smaller parts.

• The public as consumer and voter must drive the "good ship enterprise" through dangerous environmental waters ahead. We are the *demand* side of the economic apparatus that *supplies* man's goods and services; we must learn what to ask of business and government.

• The barriers to saving ourselves from ecological disaster are neither technical nor insurmountable; they are political and educational. No more formidable barriers exist.

• An integrated *global economy* with its long supply lines—the world of the future espoused by many—is fraught with hazards, as the Iraqi invasion of Kuwait and its effects on world oil supplies illustrated. The potential self-sufficiency of modern "village" life is the optimum environment for implementing entrepreneurial solutions to man's environmental problems.

• Public/consumer acceptance of the "easy" environmental solutions will catch on quickly and make wealthy some well-positioned suppliers; the "hard stuff," basic structural problems, will resist effective correction. The boldest of the enterprising will position themselves there for maximum rewards.

• Efficiencies offer the greatest opportunity for short-term solutions (and return on investment) to the environmental problem.

• Basic human needs will be met in the future, as in the past, by the biochemical process of photosynthesis carried out by green plants or sunlight. There is no other way.

• "Pollution" must be understood in its broadest terms: discarded waste of any kind, whether gas, liquid, or solid. To the fullest extent possible, waste in all its forms must be taken out of the human production/consumption process.

• Man-made environmental degradation is caused by two things: (1) discarded waste, and (2) the destruction of those ecosystems that are the machinery of life on earth.

• All advances in halting environmental degradation, no matter how significant, will be negated by burgeoning additions to populations.

The search here is for *solutions*. They are the nuggets to be sifted from the rubble of man's environmental problems. The field of search can be narrowed down by separating the environmental problem into its component parts and examining each for its causes and the extent to which it contributes to the overall problem. With the problem reduced to comprehensible size, solutions emerge; remedy the parts of the problem and the whole of the environmental problem is remedied. Approached in this manner, the solutions to man's environmental problem are to be found in the following fields:

• water and sewage
• efficiencies and waste avoidance
• communication and education
• housing
• population management
• consulting and management
• forest/wildlife management
• real estate development
• recycling and disposal
• transportation
• agribusiness
• financing
• information
• food
• job placement
• air quality
• law
• energy

Off this list jump two categories of opportunities that stand out for their *immediacy*: communications and efficiencies. The environmental problem will not be diminished until the masses of people force solutions with their purchases and votes; that cannot happen until the public is environmentally educated, a task that falls to the popular media, including the entertainment industry and advertising. More on this shortly. Efficiencies are the other quick-and-ready entree into environmental enterprise. Like some great loose clattering fuming machine from Oz, man's industry consumes and wastes far too much for the benefits derived. Tightening, tinkering, substituting, converting, refitting, rethinking—all across the spectrum of man's productive processes, consumption and waste can be dramatically reduced with no diminution of utility or service. At some point production-consumption processes will have to be changed at their core, but until this happens getting more out of less can rein in general environmental degradation and be profitable too.

As we examine the opportunities in the foregoing list, you are encouraged to lend your ideas and suggestions to the effort. Chase the opportunities noted here. Every mind and heart turned to this effort, every commitment to work intelligently in the environmental field is a step in the direction that *mankind must travel*. There is nothing crass about chasing riches; that it might contribute legitimately to the preservation of the environment necessary for us to live is a decided plus. Good intentions, volunteer work, and the aging flower child generation have taken mankind as far as they can. It's time for new generations of full-time, bit-in-the-teeth entrepreneurs to take the wheel.

CHAPTER SIX

COMMUNICATIONS

At its very heart, the environmental problem is a communications problem. No rational person wants to asphyxiate or poison himself or his children; people just do not believe that they and their kind can perish from environmental degradation. That potential is what separates the "environmental issue" from all other issues. The consequences of continued environmental degradation are not the same as the consequences of apartheid or mistreating women or skewed national balance of payments. The environmental problem is on a level all its own; it is first among man's threats and needs to be unbundled from other social issues and watched and tended to like a cobra loose in the bedroom. People don't fully understand the environmental threat, but they sense it. Public opinion survey after survey reveals that they are willing to do the environmentally right thing *to the extent that they understand what it is*. Public actions speak even louder: people buy environmental products and services where they are singled out to be so; they support intelligent environmental legislation and leadership where the choices seem clear and realistic. Contrary to the opinions of some pundits, the public will is alive and well; the audience is ready and waiting. *What's missing is the message.*

Given the knowledge and information on which to act— even when it is erroneous—the public record shows that people will respond. There is every reason to believe, therefore, that the public would do so to an even greater extent were they more fully to understand the implications of human habitat destruction; were they to be able to accurately distinguish the environmentally good from the bad, to make enlightened decisions at the point of purchase and sort out real political leadership from the rabble. In the absence of this kind of information lie tremendous opportunities for the environmental entrepreneur. Thank God that ignorance is correctable.

Simply decrying environmental degradation in its many forms does not convey what to do about it. Today's environmental message must move beyond the emphasis on wildlife and natural places to the preservation of people. If the habitat necessary to support people is salvaged, there will necessarily be natural environs and a place for wildlife. Man evolved from the wild; it is part of his make-up, and he cannot survive without it. Today's environmental message must make connections: what does the waste of the Amazon rain forest mean to a family in Paris or Melbourne? What does starvation in Africa say about food supplies in America? Today's environmental message must faithfully communicate the unvarnished *consequences* of human habitat destruction because only through *fear* will man acquire the *will* to change; it must target the root causes of the degradation and solutions to the problems. And since solutions generally come with a price tag, basic environmental economics—a new economics—must be taught. It is the adult populace that must learn the environmental facts of life; the solutions cannot be left to our children. There is not time.

Every businessman who ever met a payroll understands that there is no such thing as a free lunch. But they forget when it comes to the environment. Air is not free. Business and the general public need to understand this. Every one of us pays an exorbitant out-of-pocket price in medical bills, insurance premiums, interest rates, taxes, and other expenses for the contamination of the one and only tank of air we all breathe from. And we are going to pay even more. How is this so and what will it take to correct the problem? That is part of the message that must be conveyed.

Gasoline is terribly expensive. The traditional automobile, better fuel efficiency notwithstanding, will drive us all to the grave. How? That's part of the message. A light bulb that costs six to seven times more than a "normal" bulb but gives the same light ten times longer on seventy-five percent less electricity *is not* more expensive. Collecting plastics and glass and papers and cans is eyewash in and of itself; aftermarkets are what put the "cycle" in recycle. The public needs to understand these concepts. Government regulation is no substitute for the intelligence and power of the people. Where and how does the public exert its strength? That's the message.

When a developer tells a neighborhood group that his landfill is environmentally safe, the group must know what it takes to get a truly safe and acceptable waste handling facility. The group must know what questions to ask and the members must know when they have gotten the right answers.

The public must be able to see through the claims of the product maker and service provider and recognize a real "environmental buy" when they see one. People must be taught that there are dramatic steps that they can take right now that will cut deeply into the environmental problem, steps that in ignorance appear foolish, but in reality are wise and in their own best interest (see "Fool Things"). People must learn that there are new developments that appear to be environmental solutions but are not. There is the language of environmentalism to grasp: photovoltaics (PV), PEM fuel cells, pedestrian pockets, emission credits, environmental audits. These things will play on our lives; we ought to know what they mean.

When the environmental picture is clear in the public mind, environmental degradation will begin to turn from the precipice; not until then.

If the public is to be taught these things, *how* is it to be taught and *who* is to teach it? Bringing the masses to the classroom makes no sense, nor are there teachers enough to do the job if it did. To be accomplished, environmental education must be *popularized*, built into prevailing trends and lifestyles and kept there. That is a task that can be accomplished only by the mass communicators—television and movie producers, radio programmers, advertising and marketing specialists, music makers, game designers, recreation developers, and, yes, educators and curriculum designers. Adults *do* learn from the mouths of babes. In the aggregate, the media represented by these professions reach into every nook and cranny of humanity with a voice that is heard.

MASS COMMUNICATORS

The previously staid old National Audubon Society shows how it might be done. In 1989, Audubon spun off National Audubon Society Productions, Inc. (NASP), and placed it firmly in the hands of aggressive 43-year-old

Christopher Palmer. NASP was created "to use the mass communications media, including video, film, print, music, and software, to move a mass audience to action on environmental issues." Palmer wasted no time in showing the way to enlightening a lot of people in a hurry.

The company produces movie videos for MTV, VH-1 and other television networks. The first effort, starring no less than the Grateful Dead, was titled after the group's song "We Can Run." It was a good first effort, according to producer Claude Carmichael. "We can do better," and plans are in the works to do just that. If music can convey anything from devil worship to Christianity, who's to say that it can't spread the word about the environment?

A computer software series entitled "Audubon Wildlife Adventures" hit the market with its first two disks, one on grizzly bears, the other on whales. The games are interactive, explained developer Dennis Sullivan—players take part in solving mysteries or rescuing whales, learning while answering questions. Both products have received critical media acclaim. The New York *Times* called the grizzly bear disk "the very model of an educational software program." The key, according to Sullivan, is that it is entertaining. Two new disks are being developed on poaching and sharks. Sullivan, an independent computer software developer, sees a bright future for environmentally oriented computer games. "Acid rain, greenhouse warming . . . any of the environmental issues can be incorporated into computer games."

To capitalize on the growing market for video-based learning materials in homes and schools, NASP struck a joint-venture deal with American International Media, a subsidiary of Philips Electronics N.V., the Dutch consumer-electronics giant, to produce CD-1 programs. CD-1 is a technology that combines laser-optical disc and digital-audio disc with visual elements and computer data to create easy-to-use interactivity.

In a joint venture with Apple Computer and Lucasfilm (creator of *E.T.*), Palmer initiated an Audubon program to develop and publish video disc-based interactive multimedia science programs that focus on environmental issues. The opportunities in these technologies to interpret for the layman the realities of environmental degradation are awesome.

The Audubon Science Institute (ASI), established in 1989, trains elementary school teachers to teach environmental sciences. Forty-five teachers from the school districts of Washington, D.C., and Montgomery County, Maryland, made up the institute's class of 1990. "The institute has a big multiplier effect," said Palmer just before the 1990-91 school year. "Our graduates will reach nearly 10,000 students in the classroom this fall." The institute focuses on issues like cleaning urban pollution, preserving endangered species and wetlands, and reducing acid rain. There is even a summer "ecology camp" in the program for those teachers who are interested. ASI has been well received in educational circles and is slated for expansion nationwide.

College professors are no better prepared for teaching environmental science than elementary teachers, nor are government officials or lobbyists or business executives. Could ASI or its equivalent be expanded to reach those audiences?

TELEVISION

Audubon Television Specials, a joint venture with Turner Broadcasting System and PBS affiliate WETV–TV of Washington, D.C., moved away from nice little nature films into hard-hitting television specials on substantive environmental issues featuring top celebrities for audience appeal. Twenty million people watched "Ancient Forests: Rage Over Trees" when it aired on TBS and public television in August 1990. Millions more get the message when it shows up in home video, schools, libraries, syndication, and overseas. Narrated by Paul Newman, the hour-long special raised the substantial ire of the logging industry, which raised enough hell to get a quarter of a million dollars of advertising cancelled at TBS.

"If Dolphins Could Talk," narrated by Michael Douglas, reached another twenty million viewers in March 1990 and contributed directly to the tuna industry's reluctant ban on product caught in the widely used netting practice that inadvertently decimates dolphin populations. The dolphin special came with a toll-free telephone number that viewers could call to protest the practice. For a small fee, they could have Western Union send a Mailgram in their name to tuna industry officials. Western Union, provider of the service for Audubon, reported that the volume of calls in the two hours following the program was one of the highest in the company's history. The public watches and listens, and it reacts. "If you give people a way to act, they do," said Palmer.

MOVIES

Moving to another medium, Palmer launched into feature film production—fictional material with real environmental themes starring major actors. *The Last Elephant* is NASP's first production. Starring John Lithgow, Isabella Rossellini, and James Earl Jones, it is both an action-adventure love story and a searing indictment of ivory poaching, which destroys elephant populations in most of Africa. The movie premiered in the U.S. on Turner Network Television

August 20, 1990. In theaters abroad, it plays under the title *Ivory Hunters*. Audience response proved to be very good, enough so that Warner Bros. purchased the picture. More movies are in the making.

Rarely do environmental concerns surface in American entertainment products, yet "no industry in the world is better positioned to help educate the billions of people now sharing the globe about the need for a fundamental reordering of how society relates to the environment," says Thomas Lovejoy of the Smithsonian Institution and chairman of the advisory board of the Earth Communications Office, a Los Angeles-based organization of actors, movie directors, producers, and writers. Christopher Palmer sees the opportunity and moves to capitalize on it.

While National Audubon Society Productions remains a wholly owned nonprofit subsidiary of its illustrious parent, it is a brilliant illustration of entrepreneurial instincts of the very best sort. Palmer clearly recognized the potential of today's high-tech media to reach mass audiences with an environmental message; he knew that the audience for good nature/environmental material was far larger than the fivemillion to nine million people who make up the combined mailing list of the various environmental organizations; he understood that education and entertainment do not have to be mutually exclusive, that everyone doesn't read books or all the newspaper or watch informative television documentaries or specials. But those who don't probably do watch music videos and movies, play CDs and computer games. As Palmer says, "We have to deal with the world as it is."

The world as it is will not buy environmentalism in its entertainment product just because it's environmentalism; it must be entertainment, good entertainment. If it is, it will sell. The truth is that sex and gore and intrigue play just as well against an environmental backdrop as against the themes found in traditional television and cinema. There are many environmental messages to be conveyed and many ways to do it. The possibilities don't stop with whales and elephants and rain forests; new themes need to be developed into entertaining story lines: greenhouse warming, space exploration for a new world to move to when this one is used up, fighting off giant utilities' control of new energy sources, the nonchalance of humanity as an "environmental storm" brews around it. . . . Screenwriters and producers would never lack for fresh material. The comedy *Naked Gun 2 $^1/_2$*, starring Leslie Nielsen, proved a box office smash in 1991 with a plot built around an enlightened national energy policy. The Rocky Mountain Institute and other resource policy groups provided the expertise for a script that touched on previously esoteric issues like ozone depletion, compact fluorescent light bulbs, superwindows, photovoltaics, and solar-powered transportation.The environmental theme doesn't have to be central to the story as is the case with *The Last Elephant* or earlier "environmental classics" like *The China Syndrome* (a nuclear meltdown) or *Silkwood* (more nuclear); it can run subtly in the background and fit any era or setting. Greed and deceit were the theme of a February 1991 episode of "The Guns Of Paradise," a popular Friday-night TV western set in the horse and buggy days of the 1890s. Animals and people were dying from a mysterious illness, and a dramatic conflict arose between the townspeople and the owners of a nearby copper smelter. The mystery turned out to be water pollution (arsenic) from the smelter.

There are other initiatives under way in the environmental communications/education field that seem to verify the presence of potentially lucrative markets. TBS is breaking new ground with "Captain Planet" and "Voice of the Planet." "Captain Planet" is a sure winner in syndication for its producers, believes Henry Schuster, a TBS executive.

Raffi, every mother's cult figure, is switching heavily into music with environmental messages. Preadolescents know Raffi for his brilliant, gentle children's concerts, music videos, tapes, and records. A Canadian appreciated worldwide, Raffi has sold millions of recordings and is no small addition to those who would make their fortunes spreading the environmental word. Narada Productions, a new age music producer in Milwaukee, Wisconsin, has seen sales of its *Wilderness Collection* soar past anything the firm has produced in its twelve-year history.

Is the market ready for an environmental news network (ENN?)? Ted Turner paved the way for the genre with his bold Cable News Network (CNN). The format is acceptable, advertisers have taken on a "green" tint in this decade of the environment and should line up as sponsors, there is a sizable hard core of environmentalists to build an audience upon. The producer should do well. Syndicated portions of such a network should make money for a variety of experts. Big winners in a full-blown venture like this would be our children. The education potential of an ENN is untouchable by any other single means of communication. How about talk shows? That great American institution and cheap time-filler is a perfect forum for entertaining, in-depth discussions of the whole range of environmental issues.

EDUCATION

The Cousteau Society is working with the Department of Education of the small island nation of Papua New

Guinea to develop a ten-year curriculum in environmental education. Is there a bigger market for this service in the educational institutions of the United States, Canada, Europe, China, India, Russia? Many countries, South Africa for one, find themselves without educational material on the environment couched in their language and tailored to their environs. Who would fill this market niche?

Are there not legitimate opportunities here for environmentalists to spin off media consulting firms and training centers? Communicators and educators must learn what to teach and how to teach; business and industry ought to know of what they speak and do. Environmentalists wrote the book; they know where the bones are buried. Is it not time for them to put their knowledge to work in different ways? Is the field of environmental communications and education not fertile ground for capitalists to buy up environmental expertise for the purpose of creating such media consulting firms and training operations? Might the Rocky Mountain Institute, with all its skills in energy efficiency and environmental alternatives, be for sale? Might its work be franchisable or licensable? How about the Council On Economic Priorities (CEP)? It is building a major environmental database; there is no better monitor of businesses' record of social responsibility, an important indicator for a growing number of investors. Is National Audubon Society Productions available? There's a lot of marketable expertise.

THEME PARKS

What are the entrepreneurial opportunities in environmental theme parks, exhibits, and the management/preservation of wild and natural places? Walt Disney World's theme parks and resorts division took in more than $3 billion in 1990. Industry analysts estimate that 28.5 million visitors flooded the turn-stiles of Orlando's Magic Kingdom, Epcot Center, and Disney's MGM Studios. Knott's Berry Farm, Universal Studios, Busch Gardens, Six Flags, King's Island, Sea World— all across the land and around the world, theme parks have captured the heart of the public and a large part of its enter-tainment dollar. Can environmental messages be delivered successfully from this stage? There are those who think so.

The Living Sea Corporation, a product of Jacques and Jean-Michel Cousteau, unveiled the Parc Oceanique Cousteau in July 1989 in Paris, France. The project got off to a rocky start because of insufficient capital and, later, Europe's loss of tourism following Iraq's invasion of Kuwait, but the concept appears sound. The Cousteaus recognized the potential of envi-ronmental theme parks twenty years ago in Long Beach, California, when converting the proud old HMS *Queen Mary* into a permanent marine-oriented museum. "We learned quite a bit about the potential of education through exhibiting during the development of this project," said Leo McCarthy, coordinator of both the *Queen Mary* and Parc Oceanique Cousteau projects. Look for the Cousteaus to move further into permanent exhibits and attractions.

Sort of an "ecological Epcot Center" has sprouted from cactus country near Tucson, Arizona. Called Biosphere II, it is a futuristic eight-story-high, three-acre glass and steel greenhouse that roughly approximates planet earth in a bot-tle. Plant life, animals, insects, microorganisms, miniature marshes and oceans, and the power of the sun all work togeth-er to create a self-contained environment that can sup-port man. That's the purpose—to create a working "inte-grated bioregenerative system" that can be used in future space exploration. Eight people, four men and four women, will test the system for two years, beginning in the summer of 1991. They will "live off the land" of the enclosure, raising their own food, recycling their waste, and breathing the air the capsule produces. Biosphere II is a serious private business venture backed by a noted successful businessman, Edward P. Bass of Fort Worth, Texas. The bill for the project is expected to exceed $150 million. "Regardless of what we find out in this initial two-year enclosure, there will be tremendous accomplishments," he says. Besides adding to marketable scientific knowledge, Biosphere II is developing technologies and generating interest that can pay off in big ways. While still under construction in early 1991, the project drew 500-1,000 tourists a day. A souvenir shop on site was overrun with customers. Space Biosphere Ventures was organized to market consumer versions of technologies like the "soil-bed reactors" that purify the enclosure's air. And, if the U.S. and/or Russia ever get around to colonizing space, no one is further along in the business of portable human habitat technology than Bass's organization. Biosphere II also sits on the 2,500-acre SunSpace Ranch. It looks for all the world like the basics of a major ecological theme park somewhere down the line.

The Fernbank Science Center, a fairly innocuous planetarium set in an ancient little forest preserve near Emory University just outside Atlanta, Georgia, attracts 800,000 visitors a year. Thus encouraged, Fernbank, Inc., parent firm of the science center, has designed and funded the $43 million Fernbank Museum of Natural History. Scheduled to open in 1992, the museum should prove a strong voice for the environment in a variety of ways. With 150,000 square feet of exhibit space, Fernbank will be the only facility in the principal city of the Southeastern U.S. capable of hosting large-scale scientific exhibits. A Smithsonian Institution show highlighting the rain forests of South America has already been booked. A three-story IMAX theater screen will open with a documentary on mountain gorillas. Admission will be paid at the door. "We designed this museum from the very beginning to generate income to support its operating budget," said Kay Davis, director of Fernbank's operations.

DATABASES

Nothing is more basic to communications and education than *information*. Reliable data, facts and figures, and analyses—no industry or family of industries can function successfully without them; there will be no resolution of man's environmental problem until he has the facts at hand to know what he is doing. The environmental frontier is vast, its exploration just begun, its understanding fragmentary and rudimentary. Yet, already, there is a great, unmanageable store of miscellaneous, incomplete information that constitutes the beginning point in man's search for solutions to his most pressing problem.

"Define your terms," said Plato. In today's world, and increasingly in tomorrow's, that means databases. The role of a database is to collect information, to render it decipherable, usable, and retrievable, and to provide for its availability by those who would use it. That the data would come with a price is understandable. Databases take many forms and serve many purposes. In the environmental arena, there are databases that track shipping accidents involving hazardous chemicals and oil spills; acute hazardous accidents and incidents at manufacturing facilities; violations of permits for air, water, and hazardous waste pollution; inspections, penalties, and compliance suits; waste reduction efforts and technologies; successful environmental management practices; Superfund sites and the parties held liable for offenses; and many other facets of earth's degradation.

Generally, it can be said of all environmental databases that they are new, that they are narrowly confined to specific industries or geographic areas, and that they are incomplete and frequently poorly designed. In any such business environment there is always the opportunity for far-sighted entrepreneurs to acquire inexpensive parts and mesh them into a dominating, valuable whole. Equifax built the world's largest credit reporting database via the acquisition and assimilation of many small, local, often diverse credit reporting agencies. The firm that would roll up all available data sources on the subject, say, of hazardous waste—the whole universe of issues from its manufacture to its disposal and subsequent status—and develop a comprehensive one-stop-shop "hazardous waste database" would own a commanding position in a changing world order that requires more and more of such information. It is not difficult to see where well-conceived, market-oriented databases could carve out profitable niches in the environmental realm. Scan the entire spectrum of man's environmental problems, and the solution to every one begins with a comprehensive base of facts and history. Acid rain, greenhouse warming, water pollution, soil erosion, desertification. . . .

One database whose time has come deals with the environmental performance of private industry. Increasingly *investors* want to know a company's environmental record and plans before buying in; *consumers* in numbers large enough to be noticed at the cash register make decisions based on what they know of a firm's environmental performance. The tuna industry was turned upside down by protests over drift-net fishing; Exxon felt the consumer's wrath at the gas pump in the aftermath of the *Valdez* incident; government policymakers stand ready to reward or penalize a company's environmental actions; journalists want to know. . . . Private industry is being judged on its environmental record as never before, and the phenomenon is just taking shape. The demand for timely and reliable data, already strong, can only accelerate.

The Council On Economic Priorities (CEP) is first into this niche with its ambitious Corporate Environmental Data Clearinghouse. By midyear 1991, the operation was scheduled to produce reports on major U.S. companies, including the Standard & Poor's 500. It will profile those industries with the greatest impact on the environment—waste disposal, energy generation, and chemicals. Reports will shape government data, independent research, and company-supplied information into easy-to-read formats. Charges for the information will start at $15 per report.

Consider what the U.S. Department of Energy is doing in its Resource Assessment Program to prepare the way for commercial ventures into electricity and heat production via sunlight, wind, and other renewable energy sources. Before you can refine technologies to capitalize effectively on these power sources, you have to know a great deal about the prevalence and characteristics of the resource. Where does the sun shine the brightest and the longest? Where does the wind blow the strongest and most consistently?

Before a utility would take excess photovoltaic (sun-powered) electricity into its power lines, for example, it would want either reliable long-term solar radiation data or a good computer model to determine how well the new feed matched customer demand. If the photovoltaic (PV) system worked the best when the utility needed it least, the economics of the deal probably wouldn't make sense. But if the sun came out at a time in the utility's day when it needed the extra capacity, PV then might be viable. To answer questions like this, DOE began in 1990 to develop a database on incident solar radiation for the entire United States for the years 1961-1990. It will be the nation's first such thirty-year database ever. Instrumentation will be put in place across the country to update the database every five years. Information gathered will include the spectral (color) content of the sunlight, data that will help optimize the design of technologies like photovoltaic cells. Those firms that move into the development of alternate electricity and heat production (see "Alternate Energy") will find this data invaluable. Data from DOE's solar radiation database will be provided free, but you have to know how to track it down . . . which points out the need for another database.

Squirreled away in government and academic research projects around the world are advanced technology and data that could well fire the emergence of key environmental industries. Much of this hardware and software is tied up by major corporations that fund the research; still, many opportunities fail to see the light of day because the "technology transfer" from government-academia to the marketplace is uncoordinated and poorly handled. Is this not an invitation to organize a database to track advanced technological developments relating to one facet of the environmental problem or another and selling that information? What is the technology? What does it do? Where is it housed? How close is it to commercial application? Who owns rights to the data or technology? Can it be purchased? How much? Are licensing or franchising agreements available? There is a wealth of information to be pulled into a comprehensive "one-stop-shop" environmental opportunities database. The chance to pick up a commercially feasible solar device for the mass consumer market or a process to neutralize toxic waste or some other breakthrough technology would attract a dedicated following to this database.

Databases mean computer software. A whole new worldwide economic order is rising subtly before our eyes; it will run off computer software not yet designed. There may be no more surer route to riches than computer software targeted to the needs of environmental enterprise.

INDICES

Modern societies rely on certain indices for determining their well-being. When the Dow Jones industrial average is advancing, optimism spreads across the land. When the gross national product (GNP) turns down, businesses and consumers tighten their belts and batten down for financial hard times. Perfectly healthy crops can go unharvested, good milk can be dumped, and valuable seed-stock can be butchered for meat if the commodities exchange flashes the wrong way. When the Pollution Standard Index (PSI) rises above 300, many Californians don't go outside, and life in one of man's busiest habitats slows appreciably.

Wire service information is very big business. Electronic screens, the modern version of the old stock market ticker tape, cost subscribers anywhere from $250 to $4,000 per terminal per month. No stock brokerage firm or major financial institution in the world can function in today's fast-paced markets without at least the basic wire services of Reuters or Dow Jones. No newspaper publisher or television producer can report news of the day without a "screen." "If you can provide a service that's valuable . . . if you can help [traders] make money, wire services are a completely price-insensitive market," says one wire service official speaking for the brokerage side of the market.

The concept of quick, simple indices of far-reaching, complex activities is well established in the public mind. The market for the various reporting services is strong. And for the first time since the turn of the century, conditions are right to launch new indices that are more relevant to the human condition. The indices followed so religiously today grew out of the "new" economic order that emerged at the turn of the century. The first Dow Jones industrial stock average was published in 1884. A *real* new economic order is at hand, and the old indices are insufficient and misleading. Given today's understanding of environmental cause and effect, a rising GNP should signal alarm in the populace instead of pleasure. Same with the Dow Jones, Nikkei, and others. Traditional industry running full-bore consumes and degrades human habitat with startling rapidity. Today's indices reflect business as it has always been done in modern times.

Greenhouse warming threatens literally to change the face of the globe, yet there are no indices flashing carbon dioxide or methane levels on a regular basis so people have a sense of where they are, so they can see where remedial efforts are working or where the "same ole same ole" is not. A variety of organizations measure greenhouse gases: the National Oceanographic and Atmospheric Administration (NOAA), major municipalities like Rome, New York City, and Los Angeles. Piecemeal databases on the subject exist. What would it take to round out this information, and would the public be interested in these reports? Would the news media, "green" investors, traders, and other customers pay for this service? The bet here is that they would.

Every person on earth, and every person who will be on earth for perhaps the next 150 years, is now more susceptible to skin cancers than at any time in man's history. Would people like a regular reading of the health of the ozone level, that blanket of vital human chemistry just *one-eighth of an inch thick?* High-altitude ozone data is available, tests are conducted regularly by NOAA. The readings can be reduced to simple indices that would make for a fascinating addition to the daily news offering.

Air pollution shortens the lives, and reduces the quality of life, in cities from Bangkok to Los Angeles, Mexico City to Rome. In these and other cities, going outside is dangerous to your health many days of the year. But which days? How many days are just bad for you but not immediately dangerous? What constitutes a truly "healthy" day, and how many a year are there of those? Many cities measure ground-level ozone, hydrocarbons (evaporated gasoline), particulates, et cetera. The monitoring equipment is available, standards have been set. But only in southern California and Mexico City are there pollution indices that daily let the people know whether it's safe to go outside and play or work. California's Pollution Standard Index is an appalling sign of the times but it is imminently practical, and it is likely to find wider and wider application as pollution builds in man's principal habitats. Who would market data of this sort and the means to convey it?

Ask the Arabs about the importance of water; ask the Africans, the Chinese, the Indians, the Israelis; ask Californians and south Floridians. The message is seeping in throughout the world: water is not a "given" in the human equation. People run out of water in the damnedest places these days, and the shortfalls will grow. How about a report on principal water stocks? Note the rise and fall of key underground aquifers and above-ground reservoirs, the pollution level of important drinking water sources, the price of irrigation water, and so on. Farmers are not alone now in their age-old quest for water data.

Per capita harvest levels could be added to this list of potential indices, and there are others. All these things are tracked, records are kept; the databases are often extensive if not comprehensive. These things affect every one of us every day, yet one has to search and dig for the occasional published reference. Imagine if the stock market operated that way: the data was stored in a database but there was no effective reporting mechanism, no electronic screens, no evening news reports, no newspaper recaps of the previous day's trading activities, no analyses. The stock market wouldn't function. Neither will the environmental problem be curbed until there are enough effective indices to educate the people and keep them apprised regularly of how we are doing as an endangered species.

The GNP is a dangerously inept indicator of economic progress because it does not factor in all the costs of production. Under GNP criteria, economies like those of Brazil and the United States can strip their lands of priceless forests, destroy irreplaceable river systems in the process of "development," and otherwise diminish man's habitat, and all the while the prosperity curve points up! It is how banana republics become banana republics. There need to be indices that reflect the environmental reality of production *and* consumption *and* waste.

There is a way to do this; it's called full-cost pricing. Essentially, full-cost pricing would build into the cost of a product or service all relevant, identifiable expenses relating to its production and delivery *from cradle to grave*. Not only would the traditional expenses of material, labor, overhead, and sales and marketing go into the establishment of a price, but previously ignored costs would be included: the costs of cleaning up the air or water or land fouled by the production process, the various displacement costs associated with utilizing certain raw materials like hazardous fuels and chemicals, liability for products once—and if— they become waste.

New-age economist Hazel Henderson illustrates the concept with an aerosol can that uses CFC as a propellant. "If you were able to capture all of the costs of dealing with what's happening to the ozone layer, the additional cases of skin cancer, how many years it's going to take the ozone layer to regenerate, etc. . . . then a single aerosol can might be full-cost priced at about $12,000. Of course, it would be off the market pretty quickly." Henderson is quick to point out that full-cost pricing is not fully achievable. As the pathways leading into and out of the production process get longer and more convoluted, the ability to accurately assess true costs diminishes and blurs. As an ideal to move toward, however, the concept is quite valid and is beginning to take hold. The U.S. Congress incorporated elements of full-cost pricing in the newly enacted Clean Air Act. Who would take on the task of building a Dow Jones-equivalent stock report based on full-cost pricing?

Henderson would go even further in this business of new measures and reports for a new reality. With the assistance and support of an impressive array of responsible world leaders and economists, she has developed a Country Futures Indicator, a "national report card" that would incorporate in a Dow Jones-like average factors like literacy, health, environmental quality, bio-diversity, and income distribution. She is forming a service to publish these indicators in typical television/newspaper formats. "It may actually galvanize a new politics here in the U.S.," Henderson explained. "If every night on the news you were to hear, 'Well, our literacy rates just dropped down below Turkey, and our life expectancy just dropped below Costa Rica,' it would be bound to have an effect. And when you look at a country in [the Southern Hemisphere] in terms of these indicators, you find something interesting—a lot of these countries are going to look a lot wealthier."

How is the public to get an accurate, timely, unemotional gauge of its well-being in a deteriorating environment? How is it to protect against further deterioration in the name of progress or comfort or profit? Indices and measures placed on our breakfast tables every morning and beamed into our homes every evening is the one and best way. It's worthy news; people ought to have it and suppliers would profit. We all would profit.

Eco-labeling

No sound reverberates more loudly in the halls of commerce and industry than the silence of quiet cash registers. Nothing gets more managerial attention or elicits quicker corrective action. Consumer-driven economies rule from the point of purchase; if at that juncture, the public had a reliable way to quickly assess the environmental quality of each product or service offered for sale, the environmental problem could actually be solved. There is such a way. It's not refined yet; it's still searching for the right formula, but it is *the way* to shape the environmental practices of any free economy. The way is eco-labeling. The enterprising communications capitalist would do well to find a way into this field. The opportunities are excellent.

Currently, ecological labeling simply places a code or symbol on product packaging that notifies the consumer of some environmentally notable quality. In Germany, for example, the Blue Angel label on an aerosol product may distinguish it from others on the shelf as containing no CFCs or other environmentally harmful ingredients; displayed on paper products like toilet paper or paper towels, it would tell the consumer that at least fifty-one percent of the contents is recycled paper. Earthtrust introduced the "Flipper Seal of Approval" in 1991. Affixed to a can of tuna it notifies prospective purchasers that fishing practices employed to catch the can's contents do not harm dolphins.

Closely allied to the labeling of products is the growing practice of touting and rating retail goods in consumer guides and publications. Call it eco-rating. Britain's highly successful *Green Consumer Guide* gives star ratings to deserving products and companies. The Earthwise Standards for Environmental Evaluation of Consumer Products, designed by consumer activist Debra Lynn Dadd, rank products from the environmentally safest (the "Earthwise" rating) to those that are only a little better than standard fare (a "Non-Toxic" rating).

Ecoscale, another rating system designed to help people choose products that do the least environmental harm, uses a point scale. In each of four life-cycle phases, a product can earn zero to twenty-five points. The four phases are (1) resource, (2) processing, (3) use/consumption, and (4) disposal/recycling. A perfect environmental score would be one hundred points.

Many supermarket chains in Europe and Canada have developed their own schemes, usually with sketchy criteria. Ten leading British paper merchants developed a labeling scheme in 1990 to explain the contents of recycled paper. With rating systems like these, consumers have a chance to "vote" for the environment with their purchases. The intent, of course, is to motivate manufacturers to develop environmentally "cleaner" products and production processes. It works.

The *Green Consumer Guide* has been instrumental in Britain's recent surge in environmental sensitivity. Between November 1988 and May 1989, a national poll of Britons found that the proportion of respondents who said they had chosen a product because of its environmental qualities shot up from nineteen percent to forty-two percent. Nearly eight out of ten shoppers responding to a survey conducted for the packaging and brand-identity consultant Gerstman-Meyers, Inc., said a company's environmental reputation is important in what brands they buy; eighty-three percent said they have changed brands based on environmental concerns. "Shoppers have shown that they can turn their back on products considered environmentally unsound in a bewilderingly short time," notes *The Economist* magazine in a September 1990 environmental survey. "At least with regulation, one knows what's coming six months down the road," lamented one merchant. "Not so with environmentally enlightened consumers."

Carried to its logical extension, eco-labeling and eco-rating would reflect cradle-to-grave, full-cost accounting in the appraisal of products and services. How much virgin material goes into the making of the product and what is the cost to humanity for the loss of the resource? What harmful emissions are dumped upon mankind in the production and delivery of the merchandise? What consideration has been given to the reuse, the recycling of the item? How much energy is expended in its creation?

Factor into an ecological labeling/rating scheme all the negative environmental consequences of production and consumption and waste, and you possess a formidable marketing mechanism for shaping the conduct and practices of business. This is an ideal not likely to be achieved, but persistence in this direction, the very threat of its possibility, can forge tremendous change. The president of a major Canadian grocery chain recently recalled the many years that his government unsuccessfully pressured Procter & Gamble to make a phosphate-free detergent for the Canadian marketplace. "When we started selling [a competitor's] phosphate-free detergent, Procter & Gamble got one on the market in less than six months."

Eco-labeling and eco-rating systems should be applied not only to products but to services such as electric power and dry cleaning, to companies, and even to governments and political leadership. Where there isn't a package to affix a label, there are guides and publications to convey a rating; where there are no options for alternative supplies of a product or service (e.g., electrical power), there are inexorable pressures that flow from being labeled a societal pariah.

For the most part, eco-labeling is controlled and administered by government agencies. Blue Angel, the oldest eco-labeling program, is administered by the German federal environmental ministry. The Canadians, drawing from the successful German program, introduced the "Environmental Choice" eco-label in 1989. Japan started a more comprehensive program in 1990 called Eco-Mark. Britain, Sweden, France, and the Netherlands are working on programs, and the entire European Community is considering a pan-European Environmental Quality label. The U.S. Environmental Protection Agency (EPA) is considering an eco-labeling program but apparently doesn't want to administer it in-house. There is a crack in the door for private business. Is there some sort of joint venture possible with EPA that would provide for private administration and program implementation *and* government endorsement and enforcement? Might then other nations be interested in such arrangements? What are the licensing or franchising possibilities here?

A promising sign that eco-labeling may be going private is the introduction in 1990 of Green Seal, an American labeling program billed as a "collaborative effort among environmentalists, consumer activists, and 'expert' technical and standards agencies." Products are evaluated against carefully established full life-cycle criteria (i.e., raw material, manufacturing, consumer usage, and recycling or disposal). Once criteria are set, manufacturers and suppliers are invited to submit their products for testing. Those who meet or exceed the standards may purchase the right to use the Green Seal on their products and in their advertising. Could Green Seal be acquired? What about Blue Angel or the others? Might the acquisition and merger of small or start-up labeling/rating operations put one in a position to take a leading role in the field of eco-labeling?

The market is seemingly awash with environmental publications, newsletters, books, guides, and reports, but there are opportunities yet in this sprawling communications medium. Title III of the 1986 U.S. Superfund legislation requires that companies report "all the pollutants they emit." Complying with this requirement has been a real eye-opener for corporate America. Fran Irvin of the Conservation Foundation in Washington, D.C., noted recently, "It is painfully clear that companies have no idea of what they are releasing—no idea." General Motors, for example, buys huge quantities of a wide variety of chemicals; management *needs* to know what's in them or suffer the consequences of Superfund, including imprisonment of corporate executives.

There is clearly a place for an industrial consumers report to apprise purchasers of bulk raw material what is in the ingredients they buy, what liabilities they may be exposed to under existing environmental legislation, what environmental damage is caused whether covered by law or not, and, perhaps, what alternative material may be used in place of more harmful substances. In its 1990 environmental survey of business, *The Economist* magazine found that environmental initiatives—many of which were economically attractive—were often not taken because management time was scarce and the information necessary to determine the best environmental investments was scarce. That is an open invitation for communication specialists to step into an information void where the customer base is motivated and quite capable of paying for good service.

The University of Illinois hosted the 1990 National Student Environmental Conference, sponsored by the Student Environmental Action Coalition (SEAC). To the overwhelming surprise of hosts, organizers, and townspeople, 7,000-plus participants showed up for the two-day event, each one paying $10 to $25 for admittance. The market for environmental conferences and seminars is at least as strong as the always popular get-rich-quick and self-fulfillment offerings that ebb and flow across well-to-do societies.

Participants in the NSE conference learned the skills and tactics of organizing against various forms of environmental degradation, how to make corporations more accountable to the environment and society, how to push college procurement policies into buying "green" and endowment managers into investing with an environmental bent, how to choose career paths to reward environmentally responsible employers and penalize the irresponsible ones. Refining this kind of information into well-designed and -marketed communication pieces possesses excellent potential for entrepreneurial profit.

ADVERTISING & PR

The venerable institutions of advertising and public relations are presented with exciting new opportunities in the environmental field. Unfortunately, the opportunities hold the capacity for both good and bad. Masking environmental degradation with slick, misleading advertising and promotion is increasingly big business these days, and it will get bigger as business and government, caught in the narrowing space between public sentiment and the cost of legitimate environmental correction, turns to making pigs' ears into silk purses.

Advertising with an environmental theme is "hot," and the agencies who do it well are in demand. Dirty money? There's no law against what they do on behalf of clientele, and most of commerce and industry can't turn off its pollution and degradation overnight. Still . . . there are other opportunities.

In a world of growing environmental awareness, prob-
ing newspeople, and serious public relations and civil liabilities, the days of hiding environmental degradation are
drawing nigh. Most companies now recognize that they are
going to have to make changes. A 1991 poll by E. Bruce
Harrison Co., Inc., of the *Fortune* 1,000 companies found that
seventy-five percent had published environmental policy
statements. Publishing a statement and correcting environmental degradation are far from the same thing, but the
step is in the right direction. This is where environmental
public relations and advertising come in.

The best of the business look to communicate a company's position on complex and volatile environmental issues
and, unlike other types of PR, they play a key role in for-
mulating policy, not just in presenting it. A corporate environmental policy is of no value if it is not known and
understood by customers who can buy or boycott products,
by communities that can stop plant construction, or by local
governments and law enforcement agencies that watch
for environmental crime. It's wise, also, that the policy be
familiar to environmental groups, who can sue a company
or laud it, and to investors, who have just one more reason
to buy into a company or to avoid it.

"Environmental public relations is a plow out in front of
PR practice, and it really is breaking new ground. I don't recall
another issue becoming so universal and influential ever,"
says environmental public relations specialist Bruce Harrison
of Washington, D.C. A 1990 report by Shandwick plc, the
world's largest public relations firm, concluded that environmental services would be in more demand in the nineties
than any other specialty. The Public Relations Society of
America reports that requests for environmental informa-

tion from members of the profession moved up in volume of queries from tenth place in 1989 to fourth place in 1990.

A new kind of advertising and public relations organization is required for today's emerging environmental economy, one composed of the traditional disciplines of communications and marketing but coupled with expertise in environmental law, science, engineering, and perhaps even corporate financing. The environmental movement will advance on a foundation of law; client firms will need to navigate the maze. The processes of commerce and industry in an environmental context can be complex and steeped in evolving terminology; the consumer has to understand what's going on. Crudely marketed environmental solutions must be repackaged, retargeted, remarketed; in-house technical expertise can avoid the pitfalls of ignorance and better position unfamiliar technologies in the marketplace. Nothing positive will occur in the environmental realm without innovative financing; the more effectively an agency can function in these circles, the more valuable it is to its client.

CHAPTER SEVEN

EFFICIENCIES

If coal and oil burn at thirty-three percent efficiency (the remainder is waste), and if ten to fifteen percent of electricity is lost in transmission, and if traditional incandescent light bulbs operate at fifteen to twenty-five percent of currently available efficiency, refrigerators at ten to twenty percent, washers at twenty percent, televisions at twenty-five, air-conditioning at twenty, photocopiers at ten and computers at five percent, and if Americans alone leak as much energy through their windows every year as passes through the Alaskan pipeline, is there any question about man's inefficiency? With America's electric bill running $170 billion annually, can you envision the financial and environmental windfall possible with just a few percentage points' improvement in efficiency anywhere along the line?

If it takes 2.2 gallons of crude oil to make one gallon of gasoline and 3.2 ounces of that gallon are lost in evaporation, and just twenty ounces actually produce energy (the rest is waste), and if 400 million vehicles worldwide burn hundreds of billions of gallons of gasoline every year, is there any confusion over why Saddam Hussein brought the wrath of the industrialized world down on himself, why the Arctic National Wildlife Refuge will become a working oil field?

If it takes three gallons of fresh water to grow a tomato, six gallons to grow a *serving* of lettuce, fifteen gallons to produce the wheat in two slices of bread, twenty-two gallons for a couple of oranges, and fifty-one gallons for *half* a cantaloupe, is there any mystery why irrigated farmland like California's Central Valley goes dry? If the old computer adage is true that "garbage in equals garbage out," is it not just as true that "poison into an industrial process equals poison out?" And if corporate executives and directors are increasingly liable for these poisons and if the poisons really do "poison" people generally, doesn't it make sense to avoid the garbage in so as not to get it out the end of the process?

There have to be better, more efficient ways for mankind to live with and capitalize upon the resources he has. And there are . . . therein lie opportunities for the environmental entrepreneur.

The technologies of mind-boggling, highly profitable, low-cost efficiencies are available right now, efficiencies that can dramatically curb the degradation of man's habitat and extend its carrying capacity. For the most part, it is all quite new and just ahead of general commercial exploitation. What's needed to penetrate this cavernous store of untapped environmental riches is broader vision, some ingenuity, good business plans, full-blown commitment and skillful marketing. Lighting illustrates the point handily.

Lighting

Directly and indirectly (air-conditioning to offset the buildup of heat from conventional light bulbs), lighting consumes twenty-five percent of the electricity produced in the

United States. That's a $42 billion tab. Expanding the nation's electricity supply also absorbs scarce investments and various government subsidies totaling another $60 billion annually. One-third of all fuel consumed in this country goes into the making of electricity. Produced along with the current is one-third of all man-made carbon dioxide emissions, the principal cause of greenhouse warming; one-third of nitrogen oxide, one of the principal causes of both acid rain and greenhouse warming; and two-thirds of sulfur oxide, the principal cause of acid rain.

Against this backdrop, consider the innocuous little compact fluorescent light bulb. It burns thirteen times longer than conventional incandescent lightbulbs and provides the same light on seventy-five to eighty-five percent less electricity. Among other benefits, that's twelve fewer bulbs to buy, twelve fewer trips up and down the ladder to replace them. Replacing a 75-watt conventional light bulb with an 18-watt compact fluorescent bulb also eliminates up to 1,000 pounds of carbon dioxide emissions, eighteen pounds of sulfur dioxide, and smaller quantities of heavy metals and other pollutants.

Compact fluorescent bulbs are a little horsey in design yet; some won't fit certain lamps. That's a design problem, however, and is correctable with consumer demand. Compact fluorescent bulbs are also several times more expensive than conventional bulbs ($15 to $30 each), but all things considered—electricity savings, replacement costs, heat buildup—they actually *cost* significantly less than the "cheaper" incandescent bulbs. In fact, the net cost of compact fluorescent lighting per kilowatt-hour in commercial applications is *minus a few cents*. The bulbs are more than paid for in maintenance, labor, and air-conditioning reductions; the electricity is effectively free.

But here is the real importance of compact fluorescent lighting: if enough homes and businesses use them, a chain of benefits accrues. First, fewer electric power plants would be needed to provide the same level of customer lighting. Put another way, currently existing power plants could light up as many as eight or nine times more homes and businesses with superior-quality illumination at a cost slightly less than zero. Either way, less fossil/nuclear fuel would be required to drive power plants, which would mean less emissions to fuel acid rain, greenhouse warming, and a host of other environmental problems directly and indirectly related to the consumption of those fuels. Experts from the Rocky Mountain Institute in Snowmass, Colorado, estimate that a general conversion to compact fluorescent lighting in the United States alone would eliminate fifty Chernobyl-size power plants. Realistically achievable improvements in 1990 technology could eliminate another sixty such plants.

Secondly, the power companies, while servicing their customers more economically, would effectively make more money by selling less electricity! That's right, *avoiding* the cost of fuel, labor, maintenance, wear and tear, and the construction of new capacity is more profitable than generating new supplies of electricity. Saved electricity, referred to as "negawatts," provides a real alternative to increasing electrical generating capacity—a losing proposition for customers, for utilities, for mankind, and for economies competing in international markets. (Japan's superior electrical efficiencies provide one of the prime underlying reasons that nation's products and services outsell those of the United States.)

The energy of a "negawatt" (a kilowatt of electricity saved) is no different from the energy of a kilowatt generated, so when power company executives sit down to determine future generating needs, they have two options: they can meet growing customer demand by producing more electricity (i.e., build new plants), or they can meet growing demand with efficiency measures and forgo the addition of new plants. Electric utilities across the country and around the world are beginning to see the picture and reconsider their business strategies.

No doubt about it, the compact fluorescent light bulb is a great little idea that could make a great big difference. So why doesn't it? Compact fluorescent lighting is practical, proven, superior technology produced by sophisticated companies like General Electric, Philips, Siemens, and Panasonic. Firms like this know a thing or two about business. So what's the problem? Consumer demand, comes the answer. That may be the problem, but the market is not at fault here; there is simply no interface between the product and the consumer. That's why compact fluorescent lighting plays no major role to date in the overall fight against environmental suffocation.

"JUST BULBS"

The entrepreneurial opportunity in this promising field of efficient lighting lies in providing the interface, getting the message and the product to the market. Think about it: getting your hands on compact fluorescent light bulbs is not easy *even if you knew what to ask for.* Catalogs sell them—*The Seventh Generation, Real Goods,* and others; architects introduce them to developers now and then; some utilities give them away in various experiments, but compact fluorescent lighting is not a readily available consumer staple.

The problem is more than just product availability, however; it's consumer education and salesmanship—*you have to know why you ought to have them.* People have to be taught the benefits of efficient lighting; they have to be sold on the virtues of switching. Yet there is no effective marketing or delivery apparatus in place.

But there is an interesting little company located in New York City's lower Manhattan called Just Bulbs. It sells *just* light bulbs, any kind you need. Bulbs for boats, airplanes, homes, businesses. Customers are decorators, designers, architects, physicians, municipalities, businesses, and homeowners and renters just walking in off the street. Business is good, says owner Shirley Brooks. The secret to the 10-year-old company's success is service: light bulbs are a quick-response item, says Brooks. "People walk in or call, and they want their bulb *now*. If you got to order it, forget it. We have a 4,000-square-foot warehouse in back and can deliver right away pretty much what they want."

A light bulb store . . . who would have thought it?

What if that concept were developed into a full-fledged franchise operation that sold *just* energy-efficient lighting, related "case goods" and information? Carry the full line of residential and commercial energy-efficient bulbs. "How-to" and educational videos explaining lighting efficiencies should sell. Books and software on the subject would go. There are the latest lighting enhancements like specular reflectors, high-frequency electronic ballasts, occupancy sensors to turn off lights when people leave the room, sensors to adjust the lighting in changing daylight conditions, polarizing lenses to reduce glare and cut down on the light needed to see, top-silvered blinds that reflect sunlight away from building interiors, and other paraphernalia. Displayed and packaged nicely, they would round out the merchandise line.

A retrofit service, complete with maintenance contract,

could be offered that would switch home or business to high-efficiency lighting. Ways could even be developed to finance the customer's costs from the seventy to ninety percent electricity savings he or she would realize. The savings are real; it's just a different currency. Perhaps the power company could be induced to pay the proposed store for the retrofit from the customer's realized savings. AT&T provides a similar service for businesses that market via "900" numbers. Perhaps a new financial institution, an "efficiency bank" or environmental bank, could be developed to fund electrical efficiencies with the payback and profit coming from earned savings. More on this later (see "Financing" section).

A consulting service for new construction, including an architectural review to add electrical efficiencies where applicable, would be a natural for the proposed store. Here too, dramatic savings in electricity *and* downsized chillers, ductwork, conduits, and wiring provide a source of funds to cover the consulting work. Put these "just efficient bulbs" stores right out among the fast food/neighborhood retail concentrations in attractive, standardized storefronts so people can find them. Turn on the advertising and start selling the public on the virtues and economies of *the* lighting of the future.

There is your interface of product and consumer in a format that Americans, at least, recognize and respond to. The compact fluorescent bulb manufacturers may even step up as financial backers in such a venture.

Energy-efficient lighting is but one part of a legitimate new field of business opportunity that slowly wafts into the vague outline of a truly awesome industry—the electric efficiency industry. Ultimately a *trillion dollar-a -year* giant, in the opinion of some experts, it is an emerging industry so new that the players, the businesses to serve the market, have not yet appeared. Imagine, a trillion dollar-a-year *new* industry, full of paying customers, all the technologies to do the job, all the incentives to buy . . . and a few tentative businesses circling the periphery, looking for an opening, struggling with the question, "How do you tap this thing?"

The "just efficient bulbs" franchise is one way. Contractors specializing in electric efficiency retrofits and new construction constitute a much-needed service, as we shall see later. Another is the financial network to bankroll electricity efficiency projects (or any other efficiency that generates measurable savings that can be converted to legal tender). Power companies have already ventured into this field with the financing of electricity efficiency experiments in markets from California to New England to New Delhi, India. Rebates paid to customers for installing electrically efficient equipment, "feebates" based on the electrical efficiency of new buildings (the most efficient get the lowest utility rate and a rebate, the least efficient get a higher rate and are charged a fee to hook up to the power grid; rebates are paid from the fees), modernization grants, leases—power companies are showing unusual creativity in developing financial ways and means to capitalize on electricity savings. They are billing their customers monthly anyway; it's easy to tack on a little extra to cover a light bulb retrofit or other efficiency. The customer can't kick: the add-on is to a significantly reduced bill.

In some markets, rebates for changeovers to greater efficiencies are being paid directly to those who sell and install the equipment. *Gas* companies are even getting into the act of selling *electrical* efficiencies. They can fund the the conversions as well as electrical utilities, and gas companies have no qualms about *really* saving electricity. If gas companies can do it, so can other businesses. The possibilities get more appealing the deeper one probes in the electric efficiency industry. Unless traditional lenders and investors wake up to the potential of electrical efficiencies, they are going to lose a great piece of banking business to their friendly local power company.

MOTORS

We have examined the efficiencies currently available in lighting, new capabilities much advanced over technologies considered current as recently as 1988-89. The advances are no less impressive in the other principal segments of the industry—electric motors and appliances, including office equipment.

Electric motors use more than half the electricity generated in this country. That's more primary energy than is consumed by the nation's fleet of 140 million automobiles. The total electric bill for turning motors in the United States exceeds $90 billion annually, or about two percent of the gross national product. Efficiencies exist in 1992, above and beyond recent advances like high-efficiency motors and adjustable speed drives, to cut that bill by fully fifty percent at costs that are recovered in a year to eighteen months, in most cases. The efficiency-improvement process for motors involves a package of thirty-five "cures" that includes the correct choice of motor for the job, the right size motor, maintenance, controls to rein in unnecessary electrical consumption, and improvements to the "upstream" electrical supply apparatus and the "downstream" drive system.

Retrofitting motors with the entire package to get the biggest return on investment is rather like eating a lobster, explains world-renowned energy efficiency expert Amory Lovin of the Rocky Mountain Institute. "There are big obvious chunks like the high-efficiency motors and the adjustable speed drives, but if that is all you eat and you throw away the rest, then you are missing out on a roughly equal quantity of tasty little morsels tucked away in crevices. You have to dig for that last half of the energy savings . . . but there is great reward in doing that. You not only double the savings; you also cut the cost of the savings by severalfold because you can often get many benefits for a single expenditure. . . . The reason that saving half of the motor energy (or one-fourth of all electricity) in this country is so ridiculously cheap—paying back in about a year, in big buildings as well as in factories—is that you are only having to pay for seven of the thirty-five kinds of motor systems savings. The other twenty-eight are free by-products of those seven."

These very achievable corrections to the nation's motor stock would eliminate the need for another 150 large electric power plants, lifting a heavy burden from the bowed back of the environment.

Lovin points out that the key to achieving the full measure of currently available electric efficiencies in motors, as well as lighting and building design, is *whole-system engineering with meticulous attention to detail*. He also notes that few, if any, companies are organized to deliver such services. "Unfortunately, we are still at an early stage of developing the mature delivery systems for these technologies as integrated packages," he said in late 1990. At best, a handful of firms perform whole-system lighting retrofits, and none yet deliver a full package of drive-power efficiencies.

SERVICE "PACKAGERS"

Like the travel industry before the advent of the vacation packager, the fledgling electric efficiency industry—indeed, the entire gamut of environmental opportunities—awaits the "packager" to simplify unfamiliar and/or complex procedures and deliver turnkey services to the marketplace. The possibilities are illustrated in a variety of ways.

When the wire, rod, and cable industry fell on hard times in the early 1980s, Southwire Corporation, the largest independent producer, set two bright engineers to work cutting expenses. Over an eight-year period, tinkering with motors, changing out lighting and other energy efficiency measures, they helped reduce the company's electric bill per pound of product by forty percent and its gas use by sixty percent. Costs of the changeover were recovered in an average of two years. Between 1981 and 1988, an especially tough period when many competitors were going out of business, the company saved $40 million of energy costs, an amount that exactly equaled profits for the period. Those dedicated engineers may have saved 4,000 jobs at ten plants in six states.

Do these men possess proven, practical expertise that can be sold in other industrial settings? Absolutely. Could they make their customers money and take a real bite out of environmental degradation at the same time? You bet. Well-packaged and -marketed by a firm designed just for that purpose, might this service get a running start on competition at a time when firms are coming under more and more pressure to reduce costs *and* pollution?

Wes Birdsell, the utilities manager of Osage, Iowa, population 3,200, went to work in the early 1980s weatherizing homes and businesses and managing electricity more efficiently. Over a nine-year period, the results were startling: enough electricity savings were realized to repay all utility debt, build a substantial surplus, and cut electricity rates five times in five years. Electric rates in Osage dropped to half the average for the state. The $1,000 per household per year that the townspeople *didn't* have to spend on electricity was spent on other goods and services, strengthening the local job market and generally boosting the economy. Two big factories liked what they saw in Osage and moved in. There is a noticeable prosperity there that is not evident in nearby communities.

Does Birdsell have something to sell to other towns? Could he show town fathers where to find the money to upgrade municipal services, pay for his expertise, and leave something extra in the pockets of their constituency? Could a well-organized firm specializing in municipal electric efficiencies have a positive environmental impact while profiting handsomely too? Yes, yes, and yes.

Puget Sound Power & Light is a big power company restricted to selling its electricity solely in the state of Washington. But the company saw the profit potential in electrical efficiency applications and formed a subsidiary in 1985 to take its expertise to the marketplace. Puget Energy Services, Inc., has implemented efficiency projects for more than 50 large commercial and industrial customers in nine states and saved in excess of 15 megawatts of electricity. What used to be a million-dollar industry as recently as 1990 exploded into a billion-dollar industry little more than a year later, notes Thomas Feiler, an energy analyst at Cambridge Energy Research Associates.

Amory Lovin and his staff at the Rocky Mountain Institute have shown India's leading utility officials the only alternative they have for, someday, supplying the nation's populace with even rudimentary electrical service—electric efficiency. With 3.3 times the population of the United States, India produces one-twelfth the electricity. A five-year expansion program that would devour nearly a third of available investment capital would leave the country further behind than when it started. Instead of trying to catch up with terribly expensive generating capacity—a truly frightening prospect for the rest of humanity—Lovin proposed a litany of electrical efficiencies, including compact fluorescent bulbs. The Indian government would be better off buying the bulbs and *giving* them duty-free to customers; it would be seven times cheaper than building new power plants. The point appears to have registered. The electrical authority of Bombay, a city of ten million, is experimenting with a leasing program that would put compact fluorescent bulbs in customers' homes and businesses. Costs would be recovered in small monthly add-ons to substantially reduced electric bills.

Practical electrical efficiencies of any kind, coupled with renewable energy from solar, wind, and biomass technologies, would be a logical fit in developing nations like India. Improved irrigation pumps, efficient motors and appliances, solar devices, wind machines, energy-efficient office equipment as commercial sectors power up to get ahead—the worst thing that could happen is that India and China and other developing nations put on a push to bring electric power generation up to any level approaching that of the Western world. The atmospheric contamination that would ensue would overwhelm the human species as surely as the sun rises.

Are there not openings here for farsighted firms to take economy-level "packages" of energy efficiencies to those parts of the world where the power gap is too wide and too environmentally dangerous to bridge with new fossil/nuclear-fueled generating capacity? Fully seventy percent of South Africa is without electricity, yet the country is ideally situated to draw maximum benefits from solar technology. But because no one has provided the market with effective "packaged" solar solutions, the solution shaping up is nuclear. A water-pumping project in Morocco that serves 6,000 people proved too costly to operate with diesel generators. It was successfully retrofitted with two ten-kilowatt wind machines, keeping the water flowing at very low costs.

If, through electrical efficiencies and contributions from alternate sources of energy, the populations of poorer nations can simply light and heat small rooms and prepare basic meals, the rest of humanity would benefit immensely from the gain in tree coverage and usable habitat that today is lost to the simple expediency of survival. The wise investors of the wealthy nations should be the first backers of such firms.

OFFICE EQUIPMENT

In many thriving metropolitan areas, the fastest-growing market for electricity is office equipment: computers, photocopiers, printers, fax machines, typewriters, telephones, etc. It turns out that this stuff is not very electrically efficient. All told, it puts tremendous pressure on utilities to come up with the capacity to keep it running, and it costs employers and building owners more and more every year in electricity-related expenses. And, for the most part, it's all unnecessary. A variety of studies show that major electricity savings can be had in office equipment; the Rocky Mountain Institute can show you how to save ninety percent of office equipment electricity at a cost of zero or less. Office equipment designers, vendors, buyers, and users have just never gotten around to the opportunities in electrical efficiency. In an extensive 1990 study of the subject, the Rocky Mountain Institute found that the adoption of today's best technologies can reduce by approximately *fivefold* the electricity needed to run U.S. office equipment in the 1990s *even as it grows in volume and capacity*. The changes necessary to gain these savings need not cost extra and may even make the equipment cheaper. Cuts in the electric bill of American business would total $2 billion to $4 billion annually and several times that much in the next decade. Nine giant 1,000-megawatt electric power plants could be eliminated and many more wouldn't need to be built.

Much of the technology that provides for these dramatic energy efficiencies grew out of the development of the laptop computer. Advanced microelectronics, mass storage devices, displays, power supplies, power management systems—all these devices, and more on the way, are in or will find their way into standard office equipment inventories in the years immediately ahead, quicker if the market pushes and the regulators go to work. The latest generation of laptop and notebook-size computers uses one to six kilowatts of electricity compared to as much as 150 kilowatts and more for a standard desktop computer. The electricity savings over the laptop's lifetime will repay its modest added front-end cost. Here again, electricity savings provide the capital to make the switch. Battery-based portable computers also eliminate the considerable expense of providing for uninterruptable supplies of power and the health and liability worries of cathode-ray tubes. Most of the electricity—nearly all, in some cases—now used by laser printers and xerographic copiers can be saved without any reduction in performance. Many older telephone sets consume ninety-five watts of electricity *just sitting there*. That's $5 a month of invisible electricity expense and more than a ton of coal-generated carbon dioxide emissions every year. Five kilowatts is all the current needed to power modern electronic phones, and even that can be cut with no loss of performance. These innovations are rather simple and require no appreciable departure from normal office operations.

Substantial *indirect* savings are also realized from super-efficient office equipment. When a building's cooling and wiring capacity becomes strained by growing "plug loads," everybody pays—tenants, employers, building owner, power company, and those of us who absorb the waste of ever-increasing power generation. Jamming in millions of dollars of extra ductwork, chiller capacity, and wiring to bring a building up to electrical demand can be avoided, and tenant/employee comfort and productivity improved by replacing inefficient office equipment. It has been shown that combining super-efficient office equipment with similarly efficient lighting and windows can reduce a building's heat generation enough to eliminate entire cooling systems. Let the employer pay for the conversion to super-efficient office equipment from the electricity savings and core lease rate reductions he will realize. Or let the building owner pay for the changeover from the money he will save in *not* renovating his building. The power company could be persuaded to kick in some of the cost because it is spared the exorbitant expense of increasing capacity. Better yet, spread the expense across all three. They all benefit . . . we all benefit.

There are not yet these sorts of business deals being made, but the potential is there; it's realistic, the reach isn't that far. Real estate lenders and investors need to grasp fully the electric efficiency concept so that developers can put together the *smartest* projects *over their lifetimes*, not just the cheapest structures measured in direct construction costs. If that means working a deal with tenants to install super-efficient office equipment to keep operating expenses down and minimize building electrical and mechanical systems, so be it. A new breed of office equipment supplier needs to crank up and show the development industry the light and the way. The same can be said for office leasing and management organizations; the opportunity to gain a competitive edge is there. The profit is in the electricity savings; learn how to use it.

An eco-labeling program needs a prominent place in this field (see "Communications") *and* in lighting, motors, appliances, and even electric power generation. Put right on the face of the power bill, the computer, the motor, and the appliance the electrical "efficiency rating" of the service or device. Make the program comprehensive and reliable, turn it into a serious marketing edge, and watch the sales of electrical efficiency climb and environmental degradation ebb.

APPLIANCES

State-of-the-art electrical appliances are a key component of the electrical efficiency industry. In a 1990 report entitled *State of the Art: Appliances,* the Rocky Mountain Institute shows how to save one-sixth of U.S. electricity—the output of ninety huge power stations—with more efficient household and commercial appliances. The costs of these savings would be less than the cost of generating electricity and far less than the retail price of electricity. The biggest savings are realized in improved residential refrigeration and freezers, followed by residential laundry equipment, including associated water-heating. Substantial savings are also shown in cooking appliances, commercial refrigeration, and a variety of miscellaneous items from waterbeds to televisions. Modern televisions, for example, use up to eight kilowatts per hour of electricity when *turned off*. That's not much per television, but multiplied by America's 135 million sets, it becomes quite a lot—the equivalent of one large nuclear power plant. Rather simple techniques exist to halt this waste if consumer demand pressed the point.

Advanced insulation, more efficient mechanical systems, and various design improvements can reduce typical refrigerator/freezer electricity consumption from 1,425 kilowatts per hour per year to 200 kilowatts per hour or less. Microwave clothes dryers now in prototype stage can save seventeen percent of the energy used by conventional electric dryers; heat-pump dryers can save sixty-nine percent. Horizontal-axis clothes washers, which dominate European markets, use half the energy of the verticle-axis washers sold in North America because they use far less hot water. European washers also spin more than twice as fast as North American units, extracting more water from the clothes and reducing drying time and the electricity it consumes. About half the electricity used in commercial refrigeration can be saved with better doors and insulation, improved mechanical systems, high-efficiency motors and compressors, and the like. The result is that less current is required to prevent spoilage.

Consumers in the United States generally don't know that these products exist, and most are unknown and unavailable to the marketplace anywhere. They need to be touted, marketed, pushed. Efficient Appliances Are Us stores? Perhaps. Perhaps there are more effective ways to interface these products with buyers, but that is what needs to occur. The groundwork for the emergence of the market is being prepared. The National Appliance Energy Conservation Act of 1987 is the beginning of federal efforts to foster efficien-

cies in appliances. California's standards for appliance efficiencies are another important indication of the direction of
this budding product line. A consortium of utilities, environmental groups, and government agencies is offering a $20
million bonus to the manufacturer who develops the most
efficient and cost-effective refrigerator, one that exceeds
1994 federal standards by at least twenty-five percent.

The stakes are enormous. The appliance industry ranks
just behind housing and automobiles in industry size in the
United States. Show the consumer a refrigerator that costs
ninety percent less to operate with no loss in performance
or aesthetics, even if it costs a little more on the front end,
and large numbers will buy. Where the added costs of electrically superior appliances prove a block to budget-conscious
buyers, there is the electricity savings to help fund the purchase. An alert financial institution—an "efficiency bank"
or even the appliance store or the power company—might
pay the front-end costs of a full package of electrically efficient appliances, then take its pay from the utility bill savings. Power company rebates for the energy savings could
be paid directly to the lender; or, perhaps, the utility could
pay the appliance store directly for the merchandise and recover the advance in small add-ons to the monthly bill.

Whatever methods are eventually employed to draw on
electricity savings to fund the purchase of super-efficient
appliances, the point is this: the money is available. Who
provides the gap financing, how it's done, and other details
of the business are starting to evolve.

NEGAWATTS

The big numbers in electrical efficiencies—hundreds of
billions of dollars—create a legitimate arbitrage opportu-

nity to broker and trade electrical savings on the open market. Like copper, pork bellies, or any other commodity, saved electricity—"negawatts," as some call it—can be converted to money and traded across time and distance. The opportunity springs from developments in the field of emission reduction credits (ERCs) that were introduced in the early 1980s (see "Financing"). The idea behind ERCs, now a feature of the newly amended U.S. Clean Air Act, is to create free-market solutions to the problem of industrial air pollution rather than leave it to government to solve. The gist is that government sets emission standards that industry must meet. (One proposal would force electric power plants to cut sulfur dioxide emissions by ten million tons and nitrogen oxide emissions by two million tons by the year 2000. Hydrocarbons emitted by dry-cleaning operations and other pollutants could be targeted and so on.) Industry's response would go like this: Plant A complies with and *exceeds* the government standard by retrofitting its operation with pollution-control measures and efficiencies, thereby earning an emission reduction credit. Plant B, for whatever reason, can't meet the standard and finds itself in noncompliance. It could pay a fine and leave itself open to litigation by government, environmental groups, or others; *or* it could buy Plant A's emission reduction credit. This would permit Plant B to pollute at a level above the government standard, but the company would have to pay for the ERC to do so, a disincentive that could cost the plant its competitive edge. Eventually the firm would be forced into compliance or suffer a loss of business to more cost-efficient operations. ERC trading occurred on a limited scale among corporate giants 3M, Armco, General Electric, Exxon, and Texaco even before its inclusion in the Clean Air Act in 1991. A scattering of Wall Street brokerage firms work exclusively in ERCs and the possibilities are picking up. One of these is "negawatts," saved electricity. Saved electricity is simply the other side of the air pollution coin; curb or reduce electricity *generation* and you curb or reduce *air pollution*. For example, one utility could contract with another to save electricity and sell the excess generating capacity to the former at a price that is attractive to both parties. The commodity—the electricity—might be saved over, say, a year and routed via a connecting distribution grid to the purchaser. Additional electricity is provided the purchasing utility without the expense of building additional plants. The environment is spared the fossil fuel emissions from generating capacity that is *not* built.

Similar transactions could occur between electricity customers. A firm that has achieved substantial electricity efficiencies could sell its "saved" electricity to an *inefficient* customer. The electrically efficient customer makes money two ways: lower electric bills because of the efficiencies and proceeds from the sale of the electricity *not used*. By purchasing the saved electricity, the inefficient customer pays less than he would pay for new generation from the power company. Nevertheless, the inefficient customer pays more for energy than the efficient customer. Eventually he will lose cost effectiveness and move to become more energy efficient or risk a decline in profit or worse. Initially, the utility in this scenario gets a wash: same electricity production spread across two customers with no additions to cost for increased capacity. As the inefficient customer becomes more efficient, however, the utility begins to achieve the enviable position of servicing more customers on less power generation. Mankind benefits correspondingly.

Markets for saved electricity can be developed between nations. The Rocky Mountain Institute illustrates a match of the electrical needs of Vermont with the electrical generating capacity of the neighboring Canadian province of Quebec. Rather than buy costly power from an expensive proposed new hydroelectric project there, Vermont could bear the cost of making Quebec City's buildings and industries electrically efficient, thereby freeing up generating capacity that could be purchased more cheaply than the electricity from the proposed dam. Vermont's costs for the saved electricity *and* the efficiency retrofit of Quebec's buildings would be half the costs of purchasing the proposed new capacity, according to RMI calculations. The Canadian utility would make more profit on the deal because the saved electricity would come from generating capacity already in place and long since paid for. Quebec's business and industry would be bolstered by the efficiency retrofit courtesy of the state of Vermont, and the rest of us would benefit from the preservation of a little more human habitat.

The situation is ripe for the emergence of a negawatt brokerage industry to match saved electricity with demand and to play off electrical efficiencies against the construction of new generating capacity. (The opportunities extend well beyond electricity and should be referred to as "efficiencies trading"—see "Financing".)

Low-cost electricity that is the product of dedicated efficiency practices can be put to work driving industrial processes that currently derive power from environmentally expensive fuels like coal or oil. Examples include the ultraviolet curing of finishes, microwave heating and drying and induction heating. Electric arc furnaces produce quality, competitively priced steel at environmental costs far below traditional processes. Such "electrotechnologies" save money and fuel and reduce pollution.

The Electric Power Research Institute (EPRI), the power industry's "house" research organization, estimates that these new technologies will save as much as a half a billion British thermal units (Btu) of fuel per year by 2000, yet increase electricity use in the United States only slightly. Actually, these technologies need not *increase* electricity use at all but could be accomplished with a net *decrease*, according to comprehensive studies by the Rocky Mountain Institute, the Lawrence Berkeley Laboratory, and others. Aggressive applications of electrical efficiencies could save four to seven times the electricity that utilities plan to save by the year 2000. RMI estimates the ability to save long term about seventy-five percent of U.S.-generated electricity at an average cost of six cents per kwh—several times lower than just the cost of fuel for a coal or nuclear power plant. Even more could be saved at higher costs.

In this context, the enterprising must ask, what are the opportunities to retrofit polluting coal- and oil-driven industrial processes with saved electricity? What money is to be made in the redesign and manufacture of equipment based on electrical power instead of traditional combustion engines? Negawatt brokers should find this a highly creative field. Contractors must be organized who can do the work of retrofitting. The service must be packaged and delivered. And there is the public to be educated. All are worthy business opportunities.

The very fact that electric utilities, the quintessential American monopoly, are being reshaped from within and without creates opportunities to supply this huge industry with an array of new products and services that could not have been sold as recently as 1988 or '89. It was then that competition—an unheard-of factor in utility considerations previously—and regulatory pressures began to chip away at the hard core of electric utility pricing strategy: rate-base. The rate-base is the beginning point for all that flows from electric utilities. Add up the expenses of producing electricity, establish the "rate-base," then tack on the profit margin. Quibble with the various state regulatory agencies about the margin of profit but argue always from the rate-base. The problem with utility rate-base as a cost basis is that there is no real incentive to be cost competitive. Competitive with whom? If a widget costs $200 or $2,000, just add it in the rate-base; the profit goes on top and is assured. If someone comes to the utility with a better widget that costs $20, where's the motivation to take it into a system that's already working with the more expensive item? If it ain't broke, don't fix it—particularly if you are going to make just as much money either way. Increasingly, the rate-base way of doing business is eroding; the incentive grows to find a better, less expensive widget. No greater collection of parts and pieces and systems and methods can be found than the apparatus of electric power generation. There is a very real opportunity in the elimination of power plant electricity altogether in those applications where economics and efficiency call for a better way. Bridge lights, path lights, billboards, expressway signs, security lights, accent lighting, and remote facilities are just a few applications that lend themselves very well to photovoltaic (solar) power supplies. Wind-driven electricity-generating machines do an excellent, economical job of powering irrigation systems in the western United States. The applications for solar, wind, and other alternate sources of electricity in underdeveloped parts of the world constitute a deep, expansive market waiting to happen. The firm that skillfully "packages" and markets these alternatives to power-plant electricity will serve humanity in the truest sense and profit financially as well (see "Solar").

BUILDING DESIGN

Windows and building design are critical factors in any effort to maximize energy efficiencies and the environmental benefits they produce. These two components alone can dramatically reduce the need for man-made energy. Michael Reynolds, an innovative architect in Taos, New Mexico, has labored twenty years to "free people from the tyranny" of costly mortgage and energy bills. Far from a kook, he has developed a housing concept that relies on thick, massive walls for heating and cooling, the sun and the wind for energy, discarded tires and aluminum cans for building material, and design and positioning to make it all work. Reynolds calls his housing "Earthships," and people like them. Actor Dennis Weaver commissioned Reynolds to build a $1 million, 10,000-square-foot Earthship in Ridgeway, Colorado. Weaver's friend and neighbor, Keith Carradine, liked what he saw and signed up for a $1.5 million, 13,000-square-foot residence. Notwithstanding these extravagances, Reynolds' purpose is to develop housing that is affordable, self-sufficient, and easy on the environment. His dwellings can be constructed by unskilled builders from a kit of plans and instructions that costs less than $1,000. Occupants can live quite comfortably free of any dependence on the electric power grid.

On a different scale, the Rocky Mountain Institute conducts its far-reaching research and consulting activities from a modern 4,000-square-foot building in the subarctic environs of Snowmass, Colorado, near Aspen. The building's passive solar design and electrically efficient lighting, office equipment, and appliances produce an electric bill of $5 per month. Five dollars . . . the building is so well insulated and designed that no furnace is needed. Water consumption has been reduced through various efficiencies by fifty percent (see "Water"). The efficiency technology to achieve all this, though "old" at seven years, was paid for in energy savings within one year.

Everyone isn't going to find an Earthship or self-sustained office building to his or her liking, but the principles that make these facilities so economically/environmentally attractive have broad application in buildings of every kind, anywhere. In 1991, passive solar design can provide about forty percent of the heating needs of a typical home or small commercial building without adding substantially to construction costs. That's an important contribution when you realize that thirteen percent of all annual U.S. primary energy consumption goes into heating water and the interiors of homes and businesses.

Passive solar design—using sunlight as a utility—also provides for dramatic reductions in the most expensive energy requirement in commercial buildings: lighting. In a thoroughly sophisticated technology called daylighting, the light of day can supplement to a surprising extent the illumination derived from electricity. Skylights, atria, and conventional windows strategically placed bring light into buildings with excellent utility. Lighting controls dim or turn off interior lights in synchronization with natural light. Light shelves and computer-controlled shutters and reflectors direct soft, diffused light into building cores where there are no windows. Daylighting alone can provide thirty to sixty percent of a building's lighting needs. New developments in this field will increase that percentage appreciably.

The Solar Energy Research Institute, a branch of the U.S. Department of Energy, and various private firms are developing a system of air-conditioning that works off sunlight and water condensation, substantially reducing the electricity required to cool living and working space. "Superwindows" are available that insulate as well as eight to ten sheets of glass and let in five-eighths of visible light but only two percent of accompanying heat. They more than pay for themselves by reducing costly space-cooling apparatuses and electricity consumption. Vacuum-insulated windows provide as much insulation as a solid wall, yet are thinner and lighter than conventional double-pane windows. Electrochromic windows, covered with a special transparent coating, are darkened with a minuscule surge of electricity. Sunlight and heat that come through the window can be controlled, reducing air-conditioning in the summer and heating in the winter. Glare is reduced and daylighting enhanced.

The things that can be done with modern energy-efficient windows and passive solar design are remarkable. Again, the market for these efficiencies awaits the organizations that specialize heavily in their promotion and application. Pella, the highly successful "window store" chain with outlets across the United States, illustrates the form and style of such a venture. Educate the public about energy-efficient windows and passive design with sophisticated institutional advertising, get them to ask for the features and benefits; sell to architects, builders, developers, and building managers. Retrofits make sense in windows, skylights, and daylighting techniques. There are consulting services to be provided for new construction. The manufacturing side of the business comes with its own set of opportunities. Somewhere in all this is a place for an "architect's architect," an energy efficiency expert to go over building plans to suggest efficiencies within the context of the original design. Charges for this "eco-architectural" service can be extracted from energy savings implemented.

None of the energy efficiencies explored thus far factor in contributions from active solar technology or other "alternate" (non-power plant electricity) sources of energy. That subject is covered elsewhere in this book, but it needs to be noted here that the combination of passive solar design, active solar technology, and daylighting alone can provide up to eighty percent of a building's heating, cooling, and lighting. Couple these savings with those from electrical efficiencies and the economics get very impressive, and hope for the future of man brightens.

WATER

The availability of "fresh" water has shaped human society from the beginning. Populations have never strayed far from the water hole, the river's edge, the lake, well, or the karez. Indeed, all terrestrial life clusters close by this essential commodity. Always, populations move when the water ceases to quench the collective thirst. The Mayans moved from the grounds of their great civilization in what is now Central America. The Anastasi moved. Genghis Khan swept over what is today the westernmost province of China, killing the inhabitants and destroying the ancient karez system of underground aquifers that made life there pleasant. That was 800 years ago, and the Xinjiang Uygur Autonomous Region has never recovered. Today the Egyptians crowd in on their waning river of life. Los Angeles begins the turn back into the desert whence it came, and one way or the other, sooner or later, the populace will move.

In today's world, the *only thing* to be done about the supply of fresh water is to be efficient, to use what is currently wasted and contaminated to nourish and, thus, slow the diminution of life's irreplaceable fluid. There is not the option to simply make more fresh water, hydro-desalination plants notwithstanding. There is an unexpandable, sometimes elusive supply of potable water available and no more. Fortunately (?), the waste and contamination of water is so great, and the efficiencies to conserve it so achievable, that water can be stretched over a great many more mouths and fields with less extraction from the primary sources.

It *can* happen that way, but it isn't; the trend is quite the opposite. But while there is not enough fear out there presently, there is growing public concern. In locales once thought to be immune to water problems, anxiety mounts over drought, ground-water depletion, water quality, and shortages. The market is awakening; the timing is right to introduce water efficiencies on a broad scale. Some water basics need to be set in place first, common-sense things like not watering the desert, not washing ground to a salty death in the name of irrigation, not mixing sewage and poisons with the water you drink, and paying fair market price for an ingredient of production without which crops could not be grown and most products could not be made. Government regulation can do some of these things but not very well and not very fast, not without the wide support of enlightened voters—too many political and economic interests to placate. The single best immediate step to putting sanity into water usage is *price*. For farmers, industry, municipalities and, yes, the *consumer* to pay fair market value for water would quickly create the framework for successful management of this critical environmental problem. The vested interests and the fearful will tell you that the price would be so high that everyone would go bankrupt. The history and mechanics of free-enterprise economics say that efficiencies would flood in on the rise in the price of water. The ways and means exist in 1991 to reduce dramatically the cost of water even as its unit price rises to market demand.

A "water market" based on fair market value and open to competition would attract a wealth of managerial skills, capital resources, and innovation that is not now present in the business. One interesting possibility emerged in a recent conversation with Fred Smith, president of the Competitive Enterprise Institute, a conservative "think tank" based in Washington, D.C. When asked where he would invest his time and resources in environmental enterprise, he said, "I might get with an oil company and buy up some freshwater aquifers. Like oil, they are natural liquid assets buried in the ground. Who better than an oil company to successfully manage and sell the stuff?"

His comments reminded me of an interview I conducted for *Time* magazine during the 1974-75 recession with J. B. Fuqua, founder of Atlanta-based Fuqua Industries and benefactor of the Fuqua School of Business at Duke University. I asked where he invested his money during tough recessionary times. "Oil domes" were a favorite investment. Oil domes are the natural reservoirs of oil deposits that are the beginning point of the petroleum industry. Once the oil dome was discovered in its raw state, Fuqua would buy it. "We know the oil is down there. It isn't going anywhere. The price over the long run is only going to go up," said Fuqua in a masterful illustration of understatement. The same thing can be said for water.

Even without pricing corrections and privatization of ownership, the opportunities in water efficiencies are huge. Let's examine some basic, rather mundane water efficiencies that, packaged and marketed correctly, could add significantly to future water supplies and prove highly profitable business ventures. A simple little faucet aerator, a $2 investment at most, can save three to five percent of the water used inside a typical American home. A typical American home passes eighty gallons of water *per person per day* through its innards before discarding it down the drain into chronically overloaded sewage systems. One hundred million dwellings housing a national average of 2.3 people each, multiplied by eighty gallons of water per person per day every day is an incomprehensible volume of water. Saving three to five percent of that figure is no paltry sum. A large share of that saved water is also not heated, another reduction in the cost of water. (Taken a step further, *solar-heated* water in a typical American home would save the atmosphere the infusion of as much as 1,600 pounds of carbon dioxide emissions annually.) For $20 or less a high-performance shower head can cut the expenditure of shower water twenty-five to seventy-five percent with no loss of bathing luxury. Here too, the cost of heating the water is correspondingly reduced.

Toilets are the biggest users of water in the average home, and twenty to twenty-five percent of the water they consume is wasted unnecessarily. It is generally not understood that water's biggest use in urban areas is for transporting human excrement. Ultra-low-flush toilets are specifically designed to operate quite effectively on 1.6 gallons of water or less, instead of the 3.5 to 5.0 gallons called for in conventional units now in place in the United States and much of the rest of the industrialized world. The added cost of ultra-low-flush toilets is more than paid for in savings in water and sewer bills. Every gallon not flushed is one less gallon in need of wastewater treatment, a second major benefit for the environment. Front-loading washing machines use forty percent less water than conventional top-loading models and hold about the same amount of clothing and clean about as well. Forty percent less water is forty percent less water that has to be heated. . . .

Great statistics, but niggling stuff. Who has the time or sense of urgency to conscientiously retrofit the home or business with water efficiencies? Leave the little things to others; let's go for the grand solution, the big fix. The fact is that there are no grand solutions but efficiencies, one house, one business, one farm at a time; there is no big fix except the little things done big time. Some are beginning to realize this.

At a 1989 conference on water efficiency in Santa Barbara, California, participants reported that the cheapest and fastest way to augment water supplies is to encourage residents to install water-efficient toilets, showerheads, and faucet aerators and to use xeriscaping (low-maintenance, low-water-consuming plant life) and improve irrigation techniques for the yard.

The city of Santa Monica, California, made the decision to retrofit 12,000 homes with ultra-low-flow fixtures to conserve water supplies and reduce loads on its water treatment plant. Water savings are expected to total 835,000 gallons per day.

A Michigan hotel saved a $70,000 tap fee by installing water-efficient toilets, faucets, and showerheads. Additionally, $237,000 was saved in front-end mechanical and related construction costs and $35,000 to $45,000 was saved in annual water and sewer bills. Over eight years, the savings totaled $750,000.

The Water Conservation Office of Calvert County, Maryland, retrofitted a senior citizens center with efficient 1.6 gallon-per-flush toilets to free up sewer capacity for fifty new apartments. The program cost $16,000 to $119,000 less than it would otherwise have cost to secure water and sewer rights for the apartments.

In a variation of the "negawatt" brokerage practice described under electrical efficiencies, the city fathers of Morro Bay, California, told home builders that to get a building permit they must first save elsewhere in town *twice* as much water as they intended to use in their proposed projects. Thus motivated, builders installed water-saving fixtures in a third of the housing stock in Morro Bay in the first two years of the program. Taxpayers were saved the expense of new water treatment capacity in a water-short era. Many residents found someone at their doors ready to install for free attractive new plumbing fixtures that would also reduce their utility costs. Ultra-low-flow equipment makers and installers enjoyed a boom in business. The builders got their permits and avoided the greater cost of inflated tap fees to pay for new water treatment capacity. The benefits were widespread; a market was made in saved water just as in saved electricity.

Commodity brokers who would trade off water efficiency measures for expensive—and often outlandish—new water/sewer projects would find a world of opportunity, as would those who manufacture, supply, and install the various cures. Add to this list of beneficiaries those who would finance water efficiency transactions. Here too, as with electrical efficiencies, the money saved in efficient water applications is money that can be used to pay for the services and products that produced the savings. Who would work out the financial details? Lenders/investors who specialize in efficiency projects? Efficiency banks, environmental banks?

Booming north Fulton County, Georgia, one of the nation's fastest-growing suburban markets since the early 1980s, ran headlong into water problems in 1986. Growth simply outstripped water treatment capacity. The local court placed a moratorium on new sewer taps. With no sewage outlets, builders and developers could not get occupancy permits. New housing sales and business leasing came to a halt. Untold millions of dollars were lost while county officials worked out emergency solutions with neighboring counties. Two years later the moratorium was back. The county has limped along since then with patchwork measures while expensive new water treatment capacity is constructed.

What if the key components of a water efficiency industry had been in place to offer a quicker and easier alternative to new capacity? A sales and marketing organization to sell local residents and business owners on a retrofit of ultra-low-flow plumbing fixtures, for example? Manufacturers geared up to supply the products, installers to make the changeover, "efficiency brokers" to bring together the parties to the retrofit and, perhaps, to arrange financing with efficiency or environmental banks? Instead of automatically reaching for the bulldozer to build new capacity to pollute more water, why not first tighten up on the consumer end: move the sewage with less water. The less water, the less "wastewater" that needs to be "treated."

Faced with the enormous expense of building a new wastewater treatment facility and the loss of business and residents, could wealthy Fulton County have been induced to fund a retrofit of local residences and businesses? Might local builders and developers have been willing to kick in some of the costs? No doubt, had the option of water-efficient retrofits been available it would have been given due consideration, but the industry wasn't in place, still isn't in place. Soon enough, however, the opportunity will come again, in Fulton County, Georgia; Nassau County, New York; Maricopa County, Arizona, and everywhere else there are burgeoning population centers and conventional approaches to water problems. The market for the yet-to-emerge water efficiency industry is there and waiting. Traders and brokers in water efficiencies need to start tracking the worldwide market, sizing up the opportunities. Sales and marketing organizations need to be packaging retrofit services and refining presentations. Lenders and investors need to develop funding packages to fit the various dictates of the market. Manufacturers need to position themselves with comprehensive lines of fixtures from economy models to top-of-the-line units for the world's affluent bedroom communities. Installation capabilities must be developed, the lobbying and public education must begin. Entrepreneurs in Arizona, California, and Virginia are making moves in the "water retrofitting service business." It's coming.

"JUST WATER"

Municipal crises are not necessary to make money in water efficiencies. Where there is money to be saved, there is money to be made. The trick is in the ease and effectiveness of achieving the savings. Consider, then, Just Water stores. If the Just Bulbs merchandising concept described under electrical efficiencies makes sense as an interface between consumer and lighting efficiencies, the same approach is certainly applicable to water efficiencies. Where does a busy homeowner or businessperson pick up ultra-low-flow plumbing fixtures without wandering endless aisles of various plumbing warehouses? How does one know what fixtures are best for his or her situation? Is there a handy service that sends someone out to retrofit your home or business? How about front-end design considerations: who can review construction plans and advise the best water efficiency measures and mechanics? What about financing arrangements for major retrofits—any way to recover costs?

An attractive Just Water store, part of a large chain or franchise for purchasing and marketing clout, set down in high-traffic shopping districts alongside the fast food restaurants and branch banks, could go far in the critical task of creating a broad-based "water culture." Convenience, service, and effective merchandising would be critical to such a venture. So would consumer education. *People must know why they ought to save water* besides the personal benefit of lower water bills. Sales personnel would have to be knowledgeable. Books, tapes, videos, posters, brochures, and other information should be prominently exhibited. Stock up on comprehensive, state-of-the-art lines of efficient fixtures and display them attractively. Installation services should be offered even though most water efficiencies are simple do-it-yourself jobs. Still, older people, the infirm, the busy, and the "unmechanical" will demand it. To boost traffic volume, carry Evian, Perrier, and other leading brands of bottled water; be *the place* for the best and latest in this popular consumer product. Water purification systems are a growth industry and will remain so. What better sales outlet than Just Water stores? Water coolers ought to sell.

Rain barrels look cute in the yard, provide "free" supplemental water for the garden or flower beds and send a message to the neighborhood that the owner is doing his or her part to conserve water. A neighborhood trend could be launched. "Keeping up with the Joneses" is a powerful phenomenon that can work to the benefit of the environment.

To keep the water and sewage flowing, drain cleaners are an occasional need, but acids and corrosives come back to haunt us all. Microbes, now packaged and available to consumers, can clear the drain "naturally" and do nothing to harm water supplies or the humans and animals who drink it. Enforcer Products of Cartersville, Georgia, has emerged as a leading producer of effective, environmentally safe bacterial solutions to wastewater problems. Put these products on the Just Water store's shelves. Alongside, put biodegradable detergents, face soaps, shampoos, and other quality water-friendly cleaners.

Oasis Bio-Compatible laundry detergent provides for cleaning your laundry *and* watering your flowers, lawn, or garden. It biodegrades into a balanced mix of essential plant nutrients, including carbon dioxide, nitrogen, phosphorus, and potassium. By connecting a garden hose to your washing machine, you can capture up to 1,000 gallons of water a month that otherwise would go to sewage.

Toilet paper? Why not? It goes down the drain, adding chlorine, dioxins, chloroforms and furons to the water supply. There is toxin-free recycled toilet tissue that is now only available in catalogs. Carry it. Push it.

There are environmentally benign car wash solutions and systems that do an effective cleansing job and dramatically reduce water usage. The Water Miser Car Wash reportedly saves up to 150 gallons of water on every car wash.

It's probably a reach for Just Water stores, but waterless composting toilets might be introduced with a model or two and some literature. Generally, composting toilets facilitate nature's work in a closed, sanitary—though not always odorless—system that produces no pollutants and uses no chemicals, holding tanks, or septic systems. More than 200,000 had been sold worldwide as of the end of 1990. The merchandise line would not be complete without a full array of xeriscaping and water-efficient irrigation products and services for the yard.

Financial backing and marketing support for the Just Water venture might come from manufacturers of the various water efficiencies. The proposed "efficiency or environmental bank" alluded to earlier would be a logical source of capital.

Just Water stores would be excellent places to introduce another concept whose time, if not the product, has arrived: on-site water and sewer treatment appliances. What if little of the water used in a modern suburban home ever left the grounds of the home but, rather, was cleaned and recycled back through the house over and over again? What if the homeowner delivered into the neighborhood sewer line minimal sewage that was *already treated*? Might a *credit* for the contribution be negotiated with the water department? Better yet, perhaps a rebate could be earned to pay for the appliance? What if the local wastewater treatment plant *gained* capacity without building new facilities simply because it treated cleaner effluent? Taxes would go down, service would go up, water supplies would stretch further and further and last longer and longer.

Who would design and manufacture small, unobtrusive, aesthetically pleasing wastewater treatment plants for the home, units that sat quietly beside the house or among the shrubs as inconspicuously as the ever-present air conditioner? Features might include the routing of "gray water" to lawns and gardens and the conversion of human waste to compost for use around the house. Solar energy has been used to break down tough compounds like dioxins and PCBs; it could surely be used to break down human waste. Perhaps there is a solar application here, both as a decontaminant and as a power source for the appliance.

The possibilities are extensive and the market is as large as all the homes in suburbia, wherever they may be. The potential savings for the homeowner and the local utility are more than adequate for smart "efficiency financiers" to extract payment for the cost of the homeowner's wastewater appliance. Such an appliance would be a powerful addition to the portfolio of "efficiency traders." Not only could they sell a *reduction* of water flow to treatment facilities, they could also sell a *cleaner* effluent.

STORM-WATER MANAGEMENT

Consider the opportunities in the new industry of storm-water management. Never heard of it? Neither have many city officials in the United States now charged with correcting perhaps the single biggest cause of water pollution in existence: runoff from lawns, roofs, parking lots, streets, and construction sites. Everyone contributes to it: weekend gardeners with their pesticides and fertilizers, car owners with leaky crankcases, the casual litterbug, the site developer whose dirt silts up watersheds, the homeowner whose septic tank leaks. Rainwater falling on more and more "covered" ground increasingly runs off into the nearest ditch or stream, carrying with it the local catch of loose oil, pesticides, corrosives, and a multitude of other contaminants. Every ditch and stream finds a creek, every creek a river or lake. Cities look around and find their water supplies inexplicably lifeless, fouled, and dangerous. Where did the pollutants come from? They came from everywhere. Fish become deformed or die. Stifling algae run rampant. Carcinogens and heavy metals show up in the food chain. No-fishing signs go up. No swimming. No drinking. . . . Don't drink the water? That sign cannot go up, of course. Man must ingest the supply of water available to him, safe or not.

All of man's habitat is a collection of contiguous drainage basins. Eight nations, including some of the most polluted on earth, drain into the Danube. The surface residue of thirty states washes into the Mississippi. Half of Atlanta's drainage burbles into the thin and fragile Chattachoochee. The problem is enormous. In the United States, under requirements of the Clean Water Act amended in 1991, solutions have been left to offending municipalities—which is every municipality. Local authorities are agog. They neither know *how* nor *whether* the problem can be curbed. Storm-water management simply has not been a consideration in the development of entire cities and counties, period. Millions of dollars of local tax money will be required just to *assess* the problem, hundreds of millions will be needed to control it. "We would have to build a storm-water management system," said Manuel Maloof, chief executive of DeKalb County, Georgia, host to much of Atlanta. "The *guesstimate* for that is a minimum of $300 million."

Cities and counties are starting from scratch to address the problem of runoff, whether storm-water or sprinkler induced. Funds for the work will likely come from some sort of fee charged for rooftops, parking lots, driveways, roads, and other man-made obstructions that block water from entering the ground and hasten runoff. Parts of Florida already assess homeowners an average of about $3 per month for managing runoff. Entire drainage systems will have to be mapped. Monitoring systems must be developed to determine what flows in the drainage network. Big cities don't even know the whereabouts of thousands of drainpipes, much less what comes out of them. People will have to be induced by laws and public education to cut the source of the contaminants. Ponds of water-cleansing wetlands, now largely experimental, may have to to be built to filter water before it enters lakes and rivers (see "Microbes"). Parking lots could be replaced with new porous pavements. Islands of trees and grass may have to be built in urban areas now sheathed in concrete. "Efficiency traders" (see "Financing") should find a ready market in storm-water management solutions: trade off parking lot retrofits (non-porous to porous surfaces) or absorbent "green islands" for new water treatment facilities or other expensive public works, bring in designers and contractors to do the work and arrange the financing.

The ideas are only now taking shape, the players just starting to line up. What an opening for the environmental businessman—come up with a good solution for some portion of the storm-water management problem, put together the right package of capital, know-how, and the other resources to deliver the goods, and the market is there for the taking. Big industry. Plenty of motivated paying customers. Existing technologies to do the job. And hardly anyone out front chasing the business.

WASTE AVOIDANCE

In the emerging new economics of full-cost pricing, where waste and pollution begin to weigh on profit-and-loss statements, efficiencies take on new dimensions and create unforeseen opportunities. One of these is waste avoidance, *not* putting into a process of production those things you don't want out the other end; another is *planned* recycling, designing on the drawing board for the reuse of a product at the end of its life cycle.

Easily the smartest and most economical way to avoid being left with a lot of harmful, increasingly expensive waste is not to create it to begin with. That can be accomplished by rethinking the way things are done. Hill Air Force Base near Salt Lake City, Utah, used to strip paint from aircraft by sandblasting with toxic solvents. Blasting with reusable plastic beads now does the same job just as well at lower cost with fewer health risks for workers and no leftover pollution to deal with. In the process, a market for reusable plastic "sandblasting beads" is developed. How many other polluting industrial sandblasting applications could be converted to plastic beads? Machinery that spins and turns on ceramic or gas bearings eliminates the massive handling and disposal problem associated with conventional lubricants.

Toxic petroleum-based solvents in inks and dyes have an insidious way of seeping into the atmosphere, water supply, and topsoil. Eventually, a fair share gets eaten or otherwise absorbed by man. The results, all around, are not good. The problem could be solved by banning the products that carry the harmful substances or by removing the harmful substances from the products.

Hewlett-Packard now makes a line of laser printer ink that is water-based rather than oil-based. Some newspaper ink is formulated from soybean oil, which biodegrades and doesn't poison man's habitat. The jewel-like paints on new Volvo automobiles are water-based.

To comply with California's tough new air quality laws, body shop owners are experimenting with water-based paints and a new high-volume, low-pressure (HVLP) spray gun. The HVLP sprayer delivers a high volume of air at low pressure, putting more paint on the surface than conventional methods. Since more paint goes on the car and less into the air, the release of volatile organic compounds is reduced, sparing the lungs of man a little more corrosive. "I am surprised at the quality of the paint jobs. . . . At this point there is no difference in the work we do now and the work we were doing the customary way six months ago," says Avio Piombetti of Avio Coach Craft in west Los Angeles. "In the first month we saved thirty percent on paint and the gun paid for itself."

The Solar Energy Research Institute reports that any product made with petroleum can now be made with oils extracted from plants or garbage, including adhesives, fabrics, pharmaceuticals, industrial chemicals, and plastics. Because the oils are biodegradable, solid waste disposal problems would be reduced and petroleum-based toxins would not survive so long in man's midst.

Dry painting, a process that employs powdered paint, electrical bonding, and heat, is more than a match for traditional wet painting processes in many industrial applications. Because no toxic solvents or harmful chemicals are used, dry painting is safer and cheaper when you add in the costs of emission controls, cleanup, insurance, and other pollution-related expenses. John Deere, Ford Motor Company, and Westinghouse are some of the firms looking closely at this alternative way of painting and coating.

Laser-welded vacuum insulation has been developed that

can replace insulation now made from atmospheric-altering CFCs. Paper making becomes a witches' brew of chlorine bleaches, dioxins, heavy metals, and formaldehyde that steadily degrades man's important resources, principally water. Some of the toxic chemistry can be unraveled by taking the chlorine bleach out of the process. The chlorine is used to break down natural adhesives binding wood fibers together and to whiten the resulting paper. Unfortunately for all of us, it also leads to the creation of dioxins. Hydrogen peroxide provides the benefits of chlorine bleach without the dioxin liabilities.

MICROBES

Sewage treatment in the United States and other "advanced" societies has been judged a failure by leading biologists because the treatment process leaves potentially valuable residual sludge tainted with heavy metals and other toxins. Not only is the treated sewage unfit as an agricultural soil supplement, a sorely needed product in man's eroded habitat, but a disposal problem is created as well. While the business community awakens to the potential of industrial composting as an alternative to waste disposal (see "Composting"), the principal inhibitor to its widespread marketability is the heavy metals present in the final product. Without these, the market for the product and the processes that make it is greatly expanded.

Microbes, algae, and new wastewater treatment processes that simulate natural wetlands can solve the heavy metals problem and change a liability into a major asset (see "Man-Made Wetlands"). Enforcer Products markets septic tank bacteria that break down sewage naturally, leaving only carbon dioxide and water. Oil-eating bacteria were introduced into a 700,000-gallon oil spill in Morrow Marsh in Galveston Bay, Texas, in the summer of 1990. A month later, the area was cleared of the pollutant. Bioremediation, as this technique is called, reduces the oil to fatty acids that become food for fish and shrimp. The salt buildup on irrigated farmland can be eliminated with microbe treatment. Bacteria have proven a highly effective, natural way to control long-lived, debilitating mosquito infestation problems in the heartland of America's "rice belt." After years of costly conventional mosquito spraying accomplished nothing, the city of Stuttgart, Arkansas, turned to mosquito fighter Allen Inman. Inman relies principally on naturally occurring bacteria to kill the mosquitoes in the larva stage. He estimates that mosquito populations are down seventy-five to eighty-five percent from pre-1985 levels. "It's really quite a change in the lifestyles of people around here," Inman said. "They're doing little things that they couldn't enjoy before—like being out on the porch or working in their gardens." Inman took his bacteria to Merced County, California, in 1991 to fight mosquitoes in a larger market. The Solar Energy Research Institute experiments with microbes that could render harmless many wastes that now threaten human drinking water. The potential of microbiology in the economics of environmentalism is matched by few other business opportunities.

Sometimes waste avoidance is simply a matter of using raw material more efficiently or concentrating more attention on the pollution problem. Until recently, the paper industry used half a tree in the paper-making process and threw away half a tree; today the efficiency rate is ninety percent. Still, a lot of tree is left on the forest floor by loggers who lop off branches to get a log. Scandinavian loggers waste nothing. High-tech machines seize the tree at its base, snip it off, and chew it up—trunk, branches, leaves, and all, leaving nothing but the stump as waste.

3M Corporation has led the way in detoxifying the chemistry of its diverse operations. It does so by posing relevant questions and acting on the answers. Can a product be made using fewer raw materials so that the company doesn't have to keep warehouses full of a medley of dangerous chemicals? Can it be made using different ingredients that are less toxic? 3M has saved $482 million in the 15-year life of its "Pollution Prevention Pays" program. Monsanto publicizes plans to cut toxic air emissions ninety percent by 1992, then work for zero emissions. Du Pont proposes to reduce toxic air emissions by sixty percent from 1987 levels by 1993 and to cut carcinogens by a further ninety percent by the end of the century, then stop them entirely. Exxon is redesigning plants and operations to reduce leakage that contaminates soil, which becomes hazardous waste and a disposal problem. Some of the worse degraders of man's habitat have come the furthest in correcting their ways, showing not only that it needs to be done but that it can be done and how to do it.

The very concepts of waste avoidance and waste detoxification are only now emerging, prompted by a chain of market-making developments that include government regulation, the *fear* of regulation, consumer discontent, the prospects of lower overall production costs, and plain old good intentions. There *are* those in business who recognize that the pollution simply has to stop. The market for alternative, nonpolluting ways and means to manufacture and produce is just awakening to the possibilities. And there are products and systems and methods enough to make a big economic and environmental impact in the marketplace. The business of taking these products to the market and of developing other solutions to waste creation holds tremendous promise for those who would carve out a niche in the field of waste avoidance.

"GREEN PACKAGING"

Look at packaging. In all its many forms, packaging is a leading contributor to the industrialized world's landfill crises; it grinds up great stores of forestland for paper and cardboard, cooks vast supplies of petroleum and other chemicals into plastic, and pollutes at every step in its manufacture only to be stripped from the products it wraps and thrown into the garbage. More than half the weight and volume of grocery store merchandise is packaging, stuff you pay for and throw away. Drugstores, toy stores . . . it's the same story.

Packaging has long since evolved from a device for distribution and sizing; it is now a powerful, albeit burdensome, advertising medium. Function has become the tail on the dog of promotion. Consumers in Germany, heart of the "green consumer" movement, recently began to show their displeasure with the packaging blight by tearing it off at the checkout counter. They left the garbage in the store as a protest rather than take it home. When the trash cans overflowed in the retail stores, management called the manufacturers to come get their garbage. Thus was a message sent: cut the waste, find another way. Legislation was introduced to force new thinking at the production level. Manufacturers are starting to respond.

Procter & Gamble, the world's largest consumer goods manufacturer, introduced a fabric softener in a container that can be refilled when empty with new product sold in separate throwaway plastic pouches. Great idea. Why throw away a perfectly good plastic container simply because it's empty? Let's take this revolutionary idea a giant step further. Why not a grocery store that sells its merchandise from bulk hoppers instead of cans, boxes, bags, shrink-film, and the myriad other packages that line the aisles of conventional supermarkets?

In the canned vegetable aisle, for example, you might find Green Giant green peas in a tall, narrow quarter-ton hopper decorated with the manufacturer's colors and decals. Next to it, sporting competitive markings, an identical hopper might hold Del Monte green peas. Hoppers of the various brands and styles of corn might follow. Then beans, carrots, and so on down the line. Want a couple of "cans" of corn? Just punch up the quantity desired on the "ask me" computer prompt, and the sanitary dispenser meters the order into a plastic pouch, seals it, and slaps on a brand label and price.

On the dairy aisle, the milks and juices and other liquids would be sold from the same brand-labeled hoppers, but the product might be dispensed into reusable containers. Slide last week's plastic milk jug into the dispenser, push the "fill" button and the unit steam-cleans the bottle, fills it, heat-seals a new cap and lays on a price. Didn't bring a container? No problem; the dispenser will provide a new one, but at a price that would prompt you to remember next time. Every other liquid anywhere in the store could be sold the same way. Every brand of potato chip, corn chip, or any other loose snack food could be dispensed from hoppers. Detergents, flours, confections. . . .

With so much packaging and handling eliminated, manufacturers should be able to deliver their products at lower prices. The hopper-dispenser units would have to be adapted from existing apparatuses and computerized in the manner of the newest U.S. gasoline pumps or automatic bank teller machines. There would certainly be millions to be made in this equipment, as well as in store design. The ripple effect of business opportunities from the advent of "bulk grocery stores" would be wide and deep.

BATTERIES

A product doesn't become waste until it is thrown away. Product rejuvenation is an interim step that can be insinuated into the life cycle of certain products to prevent them from becoming harmful waste. Batteries are a ready example. The acid, lead, mercury, cadmium, and other components of conventional batteries make up one of the more toxic "packages" contrived by man. Instead of discarding batteries, why not get into the "exclusively batteries" business? Specialize in battery sales, reuse and recycling. Big batteries to small, exotic to simple . . . recharge and restore them. Where they can't be salvaged, disassemble them for recycling (see "Planned Recycling").

The product line could run the gamut from batteries for forklift trucks, golf carts, wheelchairs, and automobiles to batteries for flashlights, toys, smoke alarms, and wristwatches. Sell nickel-cadmium batteries that can be recharged up to a thousand times, "disposable batteries" that leave no toxic residue, solar-powered alternatives to electronic devices that use batteries, and battery rechargers. Organize the business to capitalize on the expected growth in electric (battery-powered) cars. Recycled plastic battery cases have been used in some European car parts. There is a ready market for the exotic chemicals and metals recovered from recycled batteries.

Exclusively Batteries stores franchised across the nation and other markets? It could work. Battery manufacturers, pressed by regulators and environmentalists, might sweeten the pot by developing rebate programs for returned batteries. A well-planned and -operated chain of stores specializing in batteries would find itself ideally positioned as interface between a rapidly evolving, rapidly growing, potentially booming industry and its market.

Pollution Equipment

Pollution control equipment is another way to curb the flow of waste into man's habitat, but it is principally a stopgap measure tacked on to the ends of processes to catch or detoxify pollutants *after they have been created* but before they are released. Notwithstanding the wisdom of avoiding waste to begin with, industry and government regulators reach first for pollution control equipment when the issue of pollution is raised. It gives the appearance of a "quick fix." Catalytic converters, electrostatic precipitators, scrubbers, and other pollution control devices are available from reputable suppliers and are tried and approved. By mandating or threatening to mandate their adoption by industry, regulators appear to be doing their jobs. With scarce management time to devote to the problem and inadequate information on what best to do, company management is all too prone to add on whatever device will get the regulators and complainers off their back. Tout the pollution control device in the press as a "farsighted environmental cure-all" and hope the critics go away for awhile.

Nevertheless, end-of-pipeline pollution controls are a legitimate means of reducing environmental contamination. Catch it before it's let loose on mankind and it cannot harm us. The controls may cost a fortune, do the job only partially, and be cumbersome to apply, but they can work, sometimes quite well. The opportunities in this market are to be found in new applications for proven pollution control equipment, improving the effectiveness and affordability of existing pollution controls, and developing new devices for catching or destroying pollutants.

Catalytic converters, under ideal conditions, are very effective at what they do—burn up harmful fossil fuel emissions. In U.S. automobiles that are properly tuned and whose motors have warmed up for at least a minute or two, catalytic converters can eliminate seventy-five to ninety percent of the exhaust-pipe emissions of nitrogen oxide, hydrocarbons, and carbon monoxide. The device has not stopped the buildup of these gases in the atmosphere, but the problem would be far worse without it. New Jersey-based Engelhard Corporation, the largest manufacturer of catalytic converters, notes in its 1990 annual report, "Catalysis is the unsung genie behind an extraordinary range of modern-day products and processes. It is critical to transportation fuels that make our vehicles go and the heating oils that keep our homes warm. It purifies the air we breathe, and is vital to the production of pharmaceuticals, plastics, detergents, vitamins, fertilizers, and fibers. The functional role of the catalyst—to accelerate the rate and optimize the yield of chemical reactions without itself being consumed—is certainly not new. What is new, though, is the unique and constantly growing range of solutions that catalysis holds for the infinitely more complex times ahead."

Engelhard points to exciting applications of catalysis in water purification and landfill incineration. It can convert waste into useful products, and renewable resources like corn, starch, and potatoes into agricultural chemicals. Oils and fats can be processed for use in salad oils, margarines, and shortening. Added to newly designed wood-burning stoves and boilers, catalytic converters make wood burning an advanced technology. The Earth Stove, produced in Tualatin, Oregon, is fifty percent more efficient and produces ninety percent fewer particulates and sixty percent less carbon monoxide than older wood stoves. When more than twenty percent of U.S. households still burn wood for heat, this is not an insignificant contribution to pollution reduction.

Power plants and industrial processors are strong candidates for catalytic converter solutions, and the technology is finding wider application in "off-road" vehicles ranging from forklift trucks and underground mining equipment to jet aircraft and construction equipment. These markets can only grow as state after state, country after country tightens down on polluting emissions.

Catalysis, incorporated in incineration and waste-to-fuel technologies, could be the missing link that renders these processes truly environmentally friendly. For example, the Black Gold Recycling System, produced by the Robert Sun Company of Nashville, Tennessee, is proving to be a fine *partial* solution to the problem of what to do with used motor oil. The problem is huge and just the most familiar segment of a larger dilemma that involves waste lubricants from paper plants, rolling mills, and every other operation that employs heavy equipment.

Used motor oil is the number-one cause of water pollution in the United States, according to the Environmental Protection Agency. One gallon of used oil can contaminate a *million* gallons of drinking water. Each year businesses, governments, and front-yard mechanics dump more than 400 million gallons of used oil into our midst, the equivalent of thirty-eight *Exxon Valdez* oil spills. More than 600,000 businesses and government agencies contribute to the problem—car, truck, and farm equipment dealers, garages and service stations, the U.S. Department of Defense, fleet owners, quick lubes. Because virtually none of these organizations possess on-site recycling capabilities, they must pay haulers to pick up the waste. If the haulers mishandle the material, the originators of the waste are liable under federal law. No insurance is available to cover these risks.

The creators of the Black Gold system seized on the problem by designing an on-site waste-to-fuel unit that burns waste motor oil at very high temperatures, producing as a featured by-product space heat and hot water. The benefits of the device are significant: no space-heat or hot-water bills for the business owner, no hauling costs associated with the disposal of the material, and no resulting liability exposure under Superfund legislation. Furthermore, businesses can build goodwill in their communities (and help keep used oil off the ground and out of the water *and* fuel their own heating systems) by offering to "recycle" other people's used oil.

EPA-approved, the makers proudly claim that Black Gold rids the environment of a major contaminant. . . . Only it doesn't. Even when consumed at 2,400 degrees Fahrenheit, the oil emits stifling levels of carbon monoxide, carbon dioxide, nitrogen oxide, and the other pollutants of fossil fuel combustion. As it now stands, the Black Gold Recycling System is neither a true recycling system nor a true disposal system. There is no recycling or disposal so long as solids or liquids are merely converted by fire to gas and then released (see "Recycling"). Many times, in fact, the conversion is worse than the original material. Plastics in a landfill are going to lie right there doing nothing for fifty, perhaps hundreds of years, but *making* plastics is nasty business and *burning* plastics is even worse. Catalytic converters added to advanced waste-to-fuel processes, whether oil burners, landfill incinerators, wood chip co-generation, or what have you, could plug the last big leak in a technology that has moved far in the right direction.

Industrial scrubbers are a different kind of pollution control. Instead of dissipating pollutants as catalysis does, scrubbers capture them. Simplistically, it works like this: smokestack emissions from fossil fuel combustion pass into a maze of ductwork where they are bathed or "scrubbed" with a mist of water and calcium carbonate (limestone). The process washes from the smoke a large part of the sulfur oxides, chloride, heavy metals, and other pollutants. Electric power companies and other large industrial operations are the target market for scrubbers. The technology is effective and proven and should have made a great deal of money for the manufacturers of scrubbers.

But profit has not materialized on the scale anticipated. For one thing, power companies have been very successful in stalling government actions that would force the use of scrubbers. Secondly, the technology is very expensive and unwieldy. Installing a scrubber has been described as attaching an industrial plant to an industrial smokestack. Scrubbers are a hundred-million-dollar purchasing decision and understandably easy to argue against. Interestingly, the electric power industry's best argument against scrubbers is that smokestack pollutants can be reduced more effectively by putting less of them into the consumption process to begin with. Lower-sulfur-bearing coal and oil, improved plant design . . . yes, *waste avoidance* has come to the electric power industry. The Electric Power Research Institute (EPRI) reports that pollution controls integrated into the design of a plant save half the cost of adding controls after construction. Cooling towers, scrubbers, electrostatic precipitators, and other end-of-pipeline controls can add forty-five percent to the capital costs of a coal-fired plant and thirty percent to operating costs, according to EPRI.

The last drawback that has worked against adoption of industrial scrubbers is this: while they extract pollutants from gaseous emissions, scrubbers give them back in waterborne emissions. The sulfur and other waste captured by scrubbers has to go somewhere and that usually means a "sulfur pond" on the user's grounds. To a power company, sulfur and other waste suspended in the water of small lakes is no less an environmental liability than smokestack emissions.

So scrubber technology to date has not fared well, but that could be changing. Power plants alone still produce a third or more of atmospheric emissions of sulfur dioxide, carbon dioxide, nitrogen oxide, and carbon monoxide; the regulatory environment seems finally on the verge of moving to cut into these levels, and scrubbers seem to be the stopgap measure of choice. Scrubber manufacturers clearly expect the 1990s to pay off for them. Smaller, less expensive scrubbers would certainly advance the prospects for the industry. But the best bet for scrubbers may be in those distasteful little sulfur ponds.

Scrubbers are mismarketed as pollution control equipment; realistically, they are recycling machines. They "catch" marketable chemicals and concentrate them close at hand; it's just that too little use is made of the gathered material. Sulfur is the basic ingredient of important products like wallboard, fertilizers, and pharmaceuticals. Sulfur mining is a billion-dollar-a-year, long-established, worldwide industry. Why not mine power plant waste? More scrubber-retrievable sulfur goes up the smokestacks of electric power plants and into the atmosphere every year than is mined annually throughout the world. The Japanese see the opportunity. The Chiyoda Corporation has developed a scrubber technology that pulls sulfur right out of the waste stream of power plants, dries it, and processes it directly into wallboard. Plants are built alongside the power plants. Eight are in operation worldwide and others are planned.

One can see the future of pollution control equipment in a recent business notification by the South Coast Air Quality Management District of California. No fewer than twenty-four rules regulating just one facet of that region's problems, volatile organic compounds, were being fine-tuned to make them easier to comply with. The rules cover everything from solvents used in cleanup operations and degreasers to gasoline dispensing, dry cleaning, and semiconductor manufacturing. Pollution control equipment of some kind or another is a logical outgrowth of the degraded conditions that force draconian actions to head off environmental catastrophe. California does not suffer air pollution problems alone; it is just the first to try to really solve the problem.

PLANNED RECYCLING

As discarded products and leftovers from manufacturing processes pile up in the environment and the makers of the waste are increasingly called to task about it, an exciting solution slowly unfolds—planned recycling. If a product is going to be thrown away eventually, why not make it easy for someone to recycle it? At the very design stage of a product's evolution, provide for its recycling upon abandonment. If the discarded product is picked up and reused, it neither litters nor degrades, no downstream environmental liabilities accrue to the manufacturer, raw-material stocks are increased by the volume of recycled waste, virgin-material requirements are reduced, lessening the drain on a depleted planet. Reprocessing economics are realized from material that is already refined, and a whole new industry is born—disassembly.

German carmakers and leading appliance makers are showing the way in the trend to planned recycling. BMW has built a plant in southern Germany to refine the production of automobiles that lend themselves to easy recycling when junked. The Z1, a two-seat roadster, was introduced on a limited basis in 1988. Plastic body panels were designed to come off easily with the removal of a few fasteners. Scrap metal dealers, who fill a big demand from mini-steel mills for waste car bodies, can quickly strip the Z1 down to its metal componentry, which is where the dealer makes his money. Shredded and sorted, the steel and iron find a ready market.

Not so with the plastic. More and more of it is designed into automobiles as manufacturers strive to reduce the weight of their products to meet mandated gas mileage, but plastics are a decided hindrance to car recycling. There are as many as sixty different kinds of plastic built into automobiles, none of it identified, all of it fastened with no thought for ever removing it. There is no good way to strip it and sort it for resale, so *nothing* is done with it. As waste, it must be disposed of, a responsibility that can cost the recycler as much as $100 a ton in the United States. Let this waste get contaminated with cadmium or one of the other toxins built into cars, and it becomes hazardous waste, which is a much higher disposal cost. All in all, the ability to make a profit in automobile recycling gets tougher and tougher because car designers and makers do nothing on their end to facilitate the process.

BMW's venture could change things. All plastic parts on the firm's 1991 line of small vehicles will be stamped so they can be grouped by type for recycling. If plastic can be sorted by basic resin type, it is likely to have greater appeal as raw material, command higher prices, and prompt more recycling, particularly if it is easier to remove. Opel, the General Motors subsidiary in Germany, has made some of the parts on its new Calabria models from recycled plastic battery cases and designed these parts for easy removal. Volkswagen and Mercedes are delving into planned recycling. Automotive windshields are beginning to get attention from designers with an eye to recycling. Currently, they cannot be readily recycled because of the sticky plastic film sandwiched inside to prevent shattering in accidents. The number of types of plastics used in auto manufacturing is likely to be reduced to facilitate sorting and recycling. Substitutions for toxins that can accidentally contaminate the recycled waste are planned.

There were more than 400 million cars on the world's roads in 1991. By 2025, the number is projected to be four times greater. All of them will go to waste eventually, and that is a lot of steel and iron and plastic and glass and chemicals. Appliances are no less voluminous or attractive as raw material if disassembly and recycling are built into their design and fabrication. Whirlpool Corporation is rethinking methods used for decades to assemble household appliances. "There is no question that we have to design for future disposability," said engineer Julius Grau. "For instance, we are looking into fasteners and will probably use fewer screws in the future because disassemblers do not like them." Look here too for plastic components to become more homogeneous and to be marked for easy grouping. Toxins and harmful substances like PCBs and CFCs will no doubt be phased out. Appliance makers are liable for them in the United States under Superfund legislation, and recyclers are left with having to dispose of expensive, highly regulated waste.

The idea behind planned recycling is to design products that can be picked clean efficiently and consumed in other processes, leaving behind as little unusable waste as possible. "We generated the idea [of planned recycling] about ten years ago but had trouble getting people to look at it until about a year and a half ago," said Herschel Cutler, executive director of the Institute of Scrap Recycling Industries. "Now it is really taking off." Michael DeCata of General Electric's plastics division endorses the fledgling planned recycling market this way: "It is our belief that in the years to come it will become impossible to develop major markets such as transportation, appliances, or buildings and construction without a clear understanding not only of material use, but reuse as well."

Think of the possibilities. Why couldn't plastic packaging be reduced to fewer types of resins and marked or coded (see "Et cetera") for easy sorting and subsequent recycling? Design glass, paper, and metal packaging the same way. Collect the waste in traditional groupings of plastics, glass, paper, and metal (see "Recycling"). Make it worthwhile for the homeowner to segregate the material by *charging* for the collection of mixed trash and *paying* for the segregated stuff. Let the recycler separate the plastics by resin types and the glass, paper, and metals by their logical groupings. With codes or markers built into packaging material, it is no stretch of the imagination to envision automated sorting equipment that "scans" streams of waste and routes identical codes into rich piles of homogeneous raw material.

Who would enter into this business with well-conceived plans, deep pockets and an eye for the possibilities? Somewhere early in the rapid evolution of the recycling way of life, the burden of segregating waste will shift from the housewife and facilities manager to the recycler with his automated sorting capabilities. Coded trash of all kinds would go into one container and be set out on the curb as in the "old days." The recycler will sort.

Keep packaging material out of the landfills. By weight it takes up thirty percent of the typical municipal dumping ground. Packaging accounts for fifty percent of all paper produced in the United States, ninety percent of all glass, and eleven percent of all aluminum. As with other efficiencies that save municipalities money, perhaps there are pollution reduction credits that can be crafted for recyclers who keep measurable volumes of packaging debris out of landfills (see "Financing").

How about housing? Could its roofs, walls, floors, insulation, and other components be designed so that they could be readily disassembled and reused in sections (walls) or units (rooms) in new dwellings? The Japanese have made major advances in manufactured housing that employ standardized room modules that can be configured in a variety of ways to create different styles. Who's to say that the same thinking cannot be extended to the eventual recycling of a house or commercial building? If not recycled this way, perhaps houses and other buildings could be designed for easy on-site conversion to basic raw material—wood, gypsum, and asphalt chips; shredded plastic, steel, and so on. One way or the other, there have to be better ways to utilize the resources tied up in man's expensive buildings. Simply creating heaps of scrap and waste everywhere there is a house or building no one wants is poor thinking and poor business. The key to mining the riches locked into houses and buildings lies in planned recycling; make it practical and efficient to recycle, and the businesses will show up to do the work.

In addition to the list of products that might be redeveloped for recycling, there are opportunities awaiting the environmental entrepreneur in the *collection* of discarded material, in its *disassembly, sorting, packaging, and distribution,* and in its *sale* and *market development*—industry has to be shown the benefits of using man-made raw materials.

The very real opportunities in planned recycling and disassembly raise an important question: would business and mankind be better off if waste and pollution were eliminated by not creating it in the first place, or does it make more sense, economically and environmentally, to design products so that a steady stream of valuable man-made raw material is created with discardation? The answer is surely "both." If there is no realistic use for a waste emission, work to eliminate it altogether by switching to different processes or by substituting nonharmful ingredients for those that are harmful. If there is recycling value in the waste of a product or its processes of production, design for its reclamation and reuse. New categories of economists, planners, and designers need to step forward to explore this question for its opportunities, and the businessman needs to be paying close attention.

CHAPTER EIGHT

RECYCLING & WASTE DISPOSAL

If you look at man's waste as *raw material*, you can't help but get some ideas. There may be more salvageable refined oil lying loose in the environment in automobile tires, plastics, discarded lubricants, and other petroleum-based products than there are known U.S. oil reserves in the ground. Billions of tires, a Mount Everest of oil stock, go untapped. One and a half billion gallons of used motor oil and billions of gallons of used industrial lubricants are an expensive, intractable waste disposal problem instead of a coveted reservoir of raw material. Americans throw out enough aluminum every year to rebuild the country's air fleet four times and enough steel to rebuild the skyscrapers of Manhattan. The usable lumber in obsolete or abandoned homes and buildings rivals the commercial forestlands of the United States. Enough usable sulfur spews from industrial smokestacks each year to make all the gypsumboard world markets could bear. Enough compost could be generated from the waste of a dozen large U.S. cities to resurface in high-grade topsoil all the barren land of sub-Saharan Africa. There is a need, compost could fill it, and microbes could render the soil safe for food crops. Might composting operations be set up in soil-depleted regions that take garbage from afar, thereby solving two problems at once?

Enough paper and wood are thrown away in the United States to heat five million homes for 200 years. Yet Third World poor strip precious human habitat—the ecological machinery of all humanity—for anything that will burn in order to survive. There's a market; there is the material of a solution. Who would convert the material to fuel form and get it to market? That firm would make a fortune and curb a critical environmental problem that threatens us all. There is retrievable ash enough from burned coal and sewer sludge to repave most of the world's roads. . . .

Nearly all of man's production and consumption produces waste, usually much more waste than utility. Coal and oil burn at thirty-three percent efficiency; that means sixty-seven percent is left as waste. The manufacture of a single ton of paper contaminates 7,000 gallons of water. For the most part, man's waste is retrievable, but not much is being retrieved. It is estimated that just one percent of plastics is captured and reused. One-fifth to one-third of paper is reused but most of that is manufacturing scraps, returned magazines, and office paper; very little recycled paper comes from the home. Mostly man's waste lies around, floats around, or wafts around doing great harm to all of us one way or the other and easing none of the demands on finite virgin resources that are necessary to maintain an environment suitable for mankind. But some people are catching on.

Discarded aluminum cans already contain the correct alloy mix for aluminum cans, and they are plentiful and available. Why not use them, reasoned the aluminum industry twenty years ago. Today, more than sixty-three percent of all aluminum cans manufactured are recycled. That amounted to fifty-five billion cans in 1990, 1.9 billion pounds of prime raw material. Fifty-five percent of the aluminum in a new soft drink can comes from previously discarded cans. In 1990, aluminum manufacturers paid approximately $850 million for waste cans—a good deal for them, nice business for the suppliers. The business of collecting waste beverage cans has advanced to the use of vending machines. Push in an empty Coke can and the machine gives you back a nickel. Several thousand of these "reverse vending machines" now stand alongside the newspaper racks and soft drink machines in high-traffic pedestrian areas around the United States. Different models collect glass bottles and plastic containers. In New York the machines have collected more than 100 million containers in a month.

Du Pont made $70 million in 1990 from the sale of fifteen chemical products gleaned from its chemical waste stream, material that previously had cost $25 million per year to dispose of. Total addition to the plus side of the ledger: $95 million. Appliance Recyclers, Inc. (ARI), of Minneapolis, Minnesota, seized on the reluctance of landfill operators to take "white goods" like refrigerators and freezers because of their contents of CFCs and dioxins. The firm developed procedures for collecting and recycling this material either as refurbished used appliances or as segregated raw material. Shredded steel and iron find ready buyers. CFCs are recovered, distilled, and resold. Hazardous waste handling techniques and software have been developed that grow in market value. In 1991, ARI operated four recycling centers across the United States, each of which processed 30,000 to 50,000 discarded appliances.

Image Carpets of Summerville, Georgia, recognized a cheap,

plentiful source of carpet fiber in discarded two-liter plastic bottles (polyethyeine terephthalate, or PET). The firm jumped on the opportunity and today is one of the largest consumesr of waste PET bottles. And the market is heating up. In December 1990, both Coca-Cola and Pepsico, the largest producers of bottled products in the world, announced that they would begin using discarded PET plastic in their new containers. Collecting and supplying waste plastic bottles suddenly starts to get pretty attractive. The wholesale price of waste PET bottles in 1991 runs about $180 to $200 a ton, up dramatically in just five years. Quaker State now buys back its used oil bottles for reuse.

Then there is Fuji Recycling Industry KK of Tokyo, Japan. The company, in conjunction with a government research lab, has developed a process that converts plastic waste into gasoline and oil. The technology reduces 2.2 pounds of plastic waste to seventeen ounces of gasoline and seventeen ounces of kerosene and diesel fuel. There are glitches yet in the process—the plastic raw material has to be properly sorted by resin type—but the potential is substantial.

Businesses set up to churn out supplies of waste plastic bottles stand to be rewarded for the initiative. Furthermore, they find themselves positioned in the forefront of recycling generally, an industry that can only mushroom in size and diversity. McDonald's Corporation announced that it would purchase $100 million of recycled paper and plastic goods in 1991. That's a pretty good indicator of the direction of the market.

As noted previously, the Chiyoda Corporation captures waste sulfur from coal- and oil-fired electric power plants at eight locations around the world and converts it into commercial wallboard. A major expense for power companies, sulfur-rich smokestack emissions are a valuable raw material for Chiyoda. The company builds its facilities right next to the power plant and taps on to the waste stream with a scrubber technology that produces hydrated calcium sulfate or gypsum. The material costs Chiyoda nothing. In Germany, which requires that "power plant gypsum" be purchased at fair market value, the company's wallboard sales have been impressive. As the regulatory machinery of the industrialized world follows the German lead, Chiyoda will find itself way out front of the competition.

Discarded automobile tires show up in Ho Chi Minh sandals, yard mulch, housing (see "Recycling"), and other creative, if limited, ways. Tires, however, are very rich raw material to be so poorly utilized. That's the way Bill Meuser of Springdale, Arkansas, sees it. Drilling for oil and gas consumes land, labor, and capital while degrading the environment. Despite the expense and degradation, petroleum products are necessary to modern lifestyles. What is not necessary, as far as Meuser is concerned, is to bury the oil and gas after having gone to the trouble of collecting it. A tire is nearly all energy; what is not is perfectly good steel and nylon cord, both of which have a market.

Extract the wealth tied up in tires without releasing pollutants and you could make a lot of money *and* solve a big waste disposal problem: that's the thinking that led to Meuser's development of the Thermal Organic Reactor (THORE). A patented system that "gasifies" tires without burning them or releasing pollutants, THORE converts a twenty-pound tire into 1.25 gallons of oil, 9.8 pounds of high-grade carbon black, and nylon and steel cord "as clean as when they went into the tire." Nothing goes out the smokestack because there is no smokestack. The process works in a vacuum at low temperatures so no gaseous emissions are produced. The oil produced possesses a very low sulfur content of 0.11 percent, well below EPA standards. Experiments with household garbage, less the glass and metals, rendered twenty percent oil and an "aqua solution" that is being analyzed for its contents and utilization. Chicken litter, asphalt shingles, medical waste, sewer sludge, and a host of other organic matter have been tested in THORE and the results are essentially the same. Meuser and his small company, Products To Oil, Inc. (PTO), struggle to become a factor in the budding recycling business. Whether they make it or not, THORE is just the type of obscure innovation that can deliver mankind from the stream of waste that threatens to engulf him.

The key to success in recycling, both for business and the environment, is "aftermarkets." There must be buyers to take in, pay for, and use the raw material of man's consumption. *Collecting* waste accomplishes nothing unless it is *reused*. Far too much of "recycled" paper, plastics, glass, and other material dutifully sorted and collected ends up where it was headed to begin with—the trash. Little industrial waste finds its way into other processes that will keep it off the ground and out of the air and water. Without aftermarkets for waste, there is no recycling, only imagery. It may ease people's conscience to feel that they are doing something to alleviate environmental degradation, but no positive results are achieved without placing waste back into production. Aftermarkets put the "cycle" in recycle. They constitute the other half of the recycling equation, the half that is largely missing in today's economy. Products and by-products from one production process that go into another process are not waste, they are *ingredients*. Capture and use the waste of the second process in a third, and so on, and the resulting loop (cycle) becomes a new economic philosophy that removes all but marginal waste from man's habitat and creates entire new industries with the traditional benefits that follow.

A confluence of events is creating markets for waste that did not exist before. For starters, it is increasingly more difficult simply to *throw away* waste than in the past. You can only pile it so high and so wide before people begin to notice. Public sentiment against various forms of pollution has resulted in more stringent siting restrictions for landfills, tougher landfill permitting requirements, laws against transporting across state lines, serious threats of fines and imprisonment, and other constraints. Consequently, the cost of conventional waste disposal is rising and will continue to do so.

As it gets more expensive to dispose of waste, the economics of reusing it become more attractive. Legislation is also beginning to require that waste material be used in various manufacturing processes. California newspaper publishers are now required by law to use at least one-fourth recycled paper in their newsprint, one-half by the year 2000. Ontario, Canada, is moving in the same direction with newspapers, soft drink bottles, and other household waste. Environmentally enlightened consumers add to the pressure for recycling with their demand for "green products" (see "Eco-Labeling"). Finally, there is the growing recognition that serious recycling is simply good business.

Recycling in all its forms is destined to become a dominating family of industries. The process has begun, but it is primitive yet. Only fragments of the requisite systems, controls, methods, technologies, and management that drive modern business are in place in recycling. They must be developed and adopted at every stage along the way to a recycling economy. Therein lie great opportunities.

How much of what type of man-made raw material is out there for reuse? Is anyone taking stock? If not, why not? How can any business run effectively without a clear picture of all available materials of production? Where are the garbage/waste analysts to quantify and qualify the contents of existing landfills, junkyards, industrial waste streams, and other sources of man-made raw material? (See "Databases".) Who would match raw material with existing users and potential users? Where's the computer software to compile, process, and report this information; to route and schedule pickup and delivery; to automate and analyze the endless store of data required of vibrant, complex markets and industries? Sales and marketing organizations must be created to "move the goods," and a new genre of commodity brokers is needed to make markets where none now exist. Where are the consultants and experts needed to provide technical services to the environmental businessman and to walk him through permitting processes and other regulatory requirements? How does man's waste get collected, assembled, sorted, graded, processed, packaged, and delivered?

Every phase of the recycling process is a business venture. The *equipment* of recycling changes daily and proliferates unimaginably. Trucks, truck bodies, containers, degreasers, oil burners, used-oil extractors, incinerators, vortex reactors, thermal organic reactors—on and on it goes across every form of waste in all the phases of recycling from collection to consumption. What adaptations are necessary for a manufacturer or processor to use waste material and what opportunities are there for researching the question and providing the adaptions?

Multiply these questions times discarded plastics, glass, paper, newsprint, metals, chemicals, inks, sewage sludge, food scraps, and so forth, and the potential of recycling becomes apparent and, to a businessman, exciting.

Many "established" recycling practices have not gone far enough and leave open opportunities for those who would do the business right. Neighborhood recycling, for example, is far from achieving its potential. Whether it's curbside pickup, neighborhood recycling centers, or drop-boxes, the practice is rife with inconvenience, lack of service, and ineffectiveness. Yet, the door is open to recycling, the public buys the concept; now someone needs to step out of this tenuous, emerging industry and take command. Private sanitation firms could do it; lawn-care companies could do it; security system businesses, Sears—any organization that is acceptable at the front door of the residential community could do it. It must be a comprehensive "one-stop-shop" recycling program, everything included: the whole package of recyclables—paper, glass, metal, plastics, and organic matter; color-coordinated recycling containers that match the kitchen decor; initial setup of the "system" and instruction from a company representative, marketing material, a newsletter on the latest developments in recycling, pickup, and anything else necessary to "mine" the waste generated in the modern home. Provide this service for the homeowner, across the board, for a tolerable monthly fee, and someone will make a lot of money. Take the same comprehensive service to business—restaurants, office buildings, service stations, banks, etc.

COMPOSTING

Composting illustrates the extent to which neighborhood recycling can be carried. As part of the recycling package, the service provider can instruct the homeowner and shopkeeper in routing organic matter to the compost pile, provide the container to get it there, provide and install the composting unit, periodically service and treat the compost, and collect it regularly for use on the customer's grounds or to sell to landscape and lawn-and-garden shops. Multiple routes of hundreds of uniform compost piles is a lot of compost. Every pound of rich compost replaces several pounds of pesticides and chemicals that currently taint our lives. It takes up to forty-three tons of topsoil to add an inch of dirt to an acre of land, so the potential market is huge. Farms around Belle Glade, Florida, alone have lost more than five feet of soil since 1924. Fully one-fifth of that priceless commodity in man's habitat—agricultural soil—has been lost since 1950.

Industrial composting is another promising recycling practice that has stopped short of where it must get, leaving openings for the environmental businessman. Proven in Europe and catching on in the United States, composting municipal garbage and sewage sludge is an eminently intelligent alternative to burying it or burning it. Eighty to ninety percent of a typical landfill is either reusable or compostable. One hundred percent of sewage sludge can be composted. The mechanics of composting on an industrial scale are essentially the same as in the back yard, only bigger. Pile up the organics, wet them down, turn them regularly, and let nature take its course. Natural decomposition reduces the mass to usable compost in about eight weeks. Seattle, Washington, composts all of its sewage sludge. Dade County, Florida, hosts the country's largest composting plant. Portland, Oregon; the village of Endicott, New York; Lancaster, Pennsylvania; Denmark; Italy—the converts to composting grow.

But the lingering problem with industrial composting is the presence of such heavy metals as lead, mercury, cadmium, zinc, and copper, and toxic organic compounds like benzene and toluene. They prohibit the use of compost where it is most needed, in agriculture. Crops and livestock would take up the toxins from the compost and pass it on to us. So most industrial compost goes to non-food-growing uses like landscaping, golf course construction, tree farms, landfill cover, road construction, and biofuels (see "Alternate Fuels"). Some recycling occurs but not to the extent that is possible. Remove the heavy metals and man's composted waste becomes the richest of commodities—the organics that convert sterile ground to fertile soil—and a truly big waste disposal problem disappears. If microbes can clean heavy metals from sewage sludge and detoxify crude oil (see "Microbes"), they can do the same for industrial compost. Who would insinuate a "microbe processing" stage into the business of industrial composting? The rewards could exceed all expectations.

MAN-MADE WETLANDS

Conventional municipal wastewater treatment falls far short of the achievable in recycling. Not only are toxic sludges left behind in the treatment process, but the "treated" water is passed on with a burden of low-level chemicals that are less than desirable. Increasingly, conventional wastewater treatment fails to keep up with the demand and need for safe, ready drinking water.

Out of this reality have emerged firms like Ecology Engineering Associates (EEA). Founded on the pioneering work of biologist John Todd, EEA has developed a wastewater treatment plant that simulates a natural wetlands. Wastewater is cleaned by bacterial metabolism and physical sedimentation. The process is powered by sunlight and the actions of carefully selected plant life. Fish, snails, and other aquatic creatures finish up the cleansing operation. The results are impressive. Todd's firm designed and operates the wastewater treatment system for the city of Providence, Rhode Island. The plant produces tertiary-quality water, eliminates fourteen of the fifteen priority hazardous chemicals on EPA's list and meets EPA drinking water quality standards for nitrogen and phosphorous. "Wetlands" wastewater treatment is clearly the wave of the future. No chemicals are introduced into the process, operating expenses are insignificant, and capital costs are ten to fifty percent of those of a conventional wastewater treatment facility.

Another firm employs the wetlands wastewater treatment process to a different end—commercial fish farming. Solar Aquafarms of Sun City, California, processes wastewater much like EEA. The photosynthetic and microbial processes that help cleanse the wastewater also create a virtual stew of single-cell proteins that prove to be excellent fish food. Here, Steven Serfling, founder of Solar Aquafarms, departs from the production of quality drinking water. Instead, he maximizes the output of fish food. The norm for raising pond-grown fish is two fish per square meter (10.76 square feet). The Solar Aquafarm process can grow up to 100 fish in the same space.

Investors have taken note. Demand for fish continues to be strong while ocean harvests are plunging because of overfishing and pollution. Chiquita Foods has bought heavily into the future of Solar Aquafarms. A pilot aquafarm now under construction will produce eight million pounds annually of golden tilapia, a hybrid specially bred for its light flavor. Wetlands treatment plants are also excellent solutions to the reclamation of tainted water from mine drainage, septic tank leakage, and agricultural and street runoff (see "Storm Water Management").

WASTE-TO-FUEL

Not to be confused with recycling are waste-to-fuel operations that burn wood chips, used motor oil, garbage, or biofuels. Burning this material does not recycle it or get rid of it; as fuel, it is mostly converted from solid or liquid to gaseous emissions (smoke) and ash. Unless the gas and ash are captured and reused, there is no recycling and no lessening of environmental degradation. Burning waste, in fact, is often more environmentally degrading than the waste in solid or liquid form. Nevertheless, there are important environmental principles at work in waste-to-fuel developments. Using man's waste for fuel gives utility and value to material that used to be shunted aside and forgotten. Secondly, every pound or gallon of waste that is used for fuel is a pound or gallon of virgin material saved. Third, the techniques and methods of waste utilization are refined, illuminating the way for others who would gather and use man's debris.

Then there is this to consider: while waste-to-fuel operations are only half-measures at present, they leave only half the problem to solve—capturing smokestack emissions or eliminating them altogether. With a good cheap scrubber or catalytic converter or practical innovation like the Thermal Organic Reactor (see "Pollution Equipment"), the waste-to-fuel business could become truly impressive pollution-fighting machinery. Developing waste-to-fuel processes that feed into a recycling loop or end with the dissipation of essentially all harmful emissions is a most worthy business objective. The parts of the machinery are out there; someone needs to pull it all together and take it to market. Who is tracking the *waste* that can be used for fuel? The possibilities are many, the inventories are large and scattered; they must be delivered to the various users and the users must be sold on the virtues of the fuel.

Peanut processors in Albany, Georgia, found themselves with mountainous piles of unsightly peanut hulls that began to draw the attention of government regulators. Someone got to thinking and called the local coal-fired electric power plant, Georgia Power Company's Plant Mitchell. "Can you burn peanut hulls along with the coal?" was the question. With some study and adjustments in procedures, the answer came back: "Yes." Several thousand tons per year have been mixed with the plant's normal fuel and burned since 1989. The plant operator realizes some fuel savings. Sulfur emissions are reduced a little. The peanut processors save on disposal expenses. It has not been a big deal for the power plant, principally because demand for its generating capacity is down. But thought is being given to expanding the peanut hulls program to include pecan hulls and wood chips. A furnace dedicated to burning just this fuel could get to be a big deal, the plant manager believes. How many other peanut processing centers are there with left-over "fuel hulls" to unload? Wood chips and sawdust burn well and are the principal renewal energy form in industrial use today. De-inked and stripped of toxins like dioxins, old newspapers could be a bountiful supply of fodder for waste-to-fuel burners.

Interject a sophisticated voyager into a fragmented,

unrefined industry ripe with opportunity, and the prizes to be taken stand out clearly on the landscape. Enter Johnny Imerman on the U.S. scrap metal scene. The dirty old scrap metal business, for all its affront to aesthetics, is established industry at its most basic and quintessential recycling, albeit primitive. The businesses are predominantly family-owned local affairs stuck out on the rough side of town. Financing is little advanced from the money box and greasy checkbook, data processing not much removed from notations in a spiral notebook. Basic equipment is the acetylene cutting torch and flatbed truck, and sales and marketing are limited to the telephone and "good-ole-boy" network. Though recycling is what scrap metal dealers do, the idea that they are *recycling businesses* does not generally register. There has been no extension of the scrap metal business into waste disposal, a natural offshoot. Except where forced by growing junkyard legislation, scrap yards simply pile what they can't sell out on the "back forty."

Johan (Johnny) Imerman saw all this differently. As a highly successful dolomite and coal mine operator in his native South Africa, Imerman knew something about extracting wealth from basic raw material. When he came to Atlanta, Georgia, in 1986 at thirty years old, the raw material he coveted was that produced by the waste of man. As Mindis International Corporation, he began buying up scrap yards: seventeen in just three years, capped off by the 1989 acquisition of the venerable old Atlanta-based London Iron and Metal works for a reported $18 million to $20 million. Imerman computerized the resulting conglomerate, brought synergy to the collection of parts, created economies of scale and placed it all in the hands of a sophisticated management team. A far-reaching in-house trading operation was set up.

With the firm's volume capabilities, including brokered material, Mindis became an important supplier to markets domestic and international. Scrap metal was merged with waste disposal and recycling, and money was made coming and going. Plastics and other recyclables were added to the menu; hospital waste became part of the disposal services.

In short order, Mindis moved far ahead of the competition. From the outset, the firm grew twenty percent *a month*. In 1988, sales exceeded $100 million. By 1989, Mindis was the largest scrap metal dealer in the southeastern United States. In 1990, at age thirty-five, Johnny Imerman sold out to Attwoods PLC of London for $65 million. He stays on as president of Mindis and moves to capitalize further on the environmental problem. When asked what *other* opportunities he sees in the environmental arena, he chuckles and passes on the question. But in the summer of 1991, Mindis acquired the old General Motors Lakewood plant near the Atlanta airport. The 1.75 million-square-foot facility assembled Chevrolet Caprices and employed 2,100 workers before it was closed a year earlier. Mindis will turn the complex into the company's corporate headquarters and "the world's largest integrated recycling plant," employing 250 to 500 workers. In keeping with his nature, Imerman provides no details of the "integrated recycling" that will be done. But with a facility like that, he is likely to elevate recycling to unprecedented levels.

In many basic ways, the scrap metal business mirrors the current state of recycling in general. Every waste commodity, every facet of the enterprise built around it, awaits the entrepreneur who will consolidate the business, instill it with vigor and direction, and move it into a position to compete on a comprehensive, sophisticated level.

As the cost of demolition waste disposal soared in the U.S., National Gypsum brought technology devised to recycle scrap in its manufacturing process to demolition sites to recycle shattered wallboard. Could that technology be purchased and developed into an on-site demolition recycling business? Would the system work for other material?

The Solar Energy Research Institute has developed a thermal solar energy system that detoxifies some of man's most insidious and intractable chemical pollutants, including PCBs. The system mixes a catalyst with waterborne toxins and runs the solution through transparent piping centered in a parabolic solar energy collector. The sun's energy is magnified and concentrated in tremendous intensities on the piped liquid until it breaks down molecularly into harmless water and carbon dioxide. Want to make some money? Get your hands on this technology, develop it on a grand scale, and set about disposing of industry's brooding stock of hazardous waste chemicals. Industry will pay and pay big to be finally relieved of the liability.

Give back to mankind the space taken up in his living quarters by toxins he cannot live with. Who's to say that nuclear waste cannot finally be detoxified and/or reused, thus eliminating the principal reason why nuclear power plants should not be allowed in our midst? Burnt fossil fuel that did not exhaust into our living space would be no threat. Who would take on these commercial challenges?

With the certain advent of new generations of recycling technology, old landfills could easily become valuable "mines" of raw material that are bought and sold like timberland or oil fields; and, for a variety of good reasons, not the least of which is that they are bad business, landfills *per se* would become a thing of the past in all but the most primitive societies. In lieu of landfills, "garbage factories" of the most sophisticated capabilities would take in man's waste and churn out raw material emitting nothing into the atmosphere, water, or land. What could not be squeezed from the waste stream—an eighty percent reduction is feasible, according to estimates—would be disposed of in engineering marvels that rival yesterday's great dams, space programs, and other triumphs of man's ingenuity. And the waste would be disposed of so that it could be retrieved. Inventories would be kept. When technologies come round that can make use of the material, and/or when markets for it emerge, the stored waste could be pulled from inventory and used or detoxified.

Recycling in 1992 is advanced science and space-age technology in its formative stages. Don't be misled by the shaky start; join in, shoot for the moon.

CHAPTER NINE

TRANSPORTATION & REAL ESTATE DEVELOPMENT

Let's look at why the transportation industry is going to change and change dramatically.

As of the invasion of Kuwait by Iraq in August 1990, the United States had squirreled away 600 million barrels of oil in the U.S. Strategic Petroleum Reserve against just such an event. Smart move; our own emergency supply, enough oil even to sell our allies if need be. Sprawled across thousands of square miles of east Texas, Louisiana, and Mississippi, contained in a $20 billion system of salt caverns and support facilities, the U.S. reserves provided a lot of comfort to the American public and the entire free world. But if those 600 million barrels of oil were refined into gasoline, they would last the American public, at 1990 levels of gasoline consumption, a grand total of 31.43 days. *Days* . . . One month. All that oil, all that expense, and just one month of gasoline! U.S. motorists burn 300 million gallons of gasoline *every day*. Of all the petroleum used by the United States, sixty-seven percent goes to transportation, up from fifty percent in 1973. In 1988, transportation consumed more oil than the nation produced. No society can run fast enough to keep up with that kind of consumption. History will look back on the last half of the twentieth century in anger and shame. The profligacy of man's consumption and waste, particularly in oil, is without bounds. Oil is finite. Loose in the air, the residue of oil is poisonous. Yet it is priced and squandered as though it were endless and safe. Automobiles cause more air pollution than any other human activity. Worldwide, twenty percent of greenhouse warming is caused by automobiles and light trucks. Seventy-five percent of carbon monoxide released in the United States comes from gasoline-powered vehicles.

Converting those 600 million barrels of Strategic Petroleum Reserve crude oil into gasoline will loose into the atmosphere, among other pollutants, 175 billion tons of sulfur. Burned in cars, trucks, buses, planes, and trains, the gasoline derived from the crude will become 273 million tons of airborne carbon and additional millions of tons of other debris . . . and the atmosphere dims a little further, the chest of man draws a little tighter. And that's just *one month*. Do that every month, every year; lay down more roadbed so more cars can do more of it; add in unified Europe, Britain, Japan, Brazil, India, and every other motorized country, and the consumption and waste goes off the scale of comprehension. There is not enough recoverable oil for it to be sustained. More importantly, people cannot long survive in a closed house with an internal combustion engine running full-bore in the living room.

But we can't just quit. Shut off the oil to the industrialized world and the clock is turned back on mankind a hundred years. Modern man, after all, is *motorized* man. Entire cultures, the United States foremost, are predicated on motorized mobility. The so-called love affair between Americans and their cars is a misperception. Americans *need* their cars in order to function in a geographically sprawling society built on gasoline-powered mobility. What began as a novelty became a convenience, then a necessity, and finally a trap.

Seventy percent of the U.S. population lives in the city and immediate environs. Home in the suburbs, a singular creation of the automobile, is typically fifteen to fifty miles from the job. A normal workday may take a salesman 150 miles without his ever leaving the metro area. The sprawl of Los Angeles stretches nearly 200 miles along the coastal plain of the Pacific Ocean. The dimensions of the city would shrink two-thirds without the roadways and parking lots and decks located there to accommodate cars. It's more than sixty miles from the farthest reach of Atlanta's northern suburbs to the boundaries of its southern suburbs. The New York City metropolitan area spills over into the northwest quadrant of New Jersey, southwest Connecticut and the eastern half of Long Island—an unbroken urbanized area roughly the size of Belgium. In Chicago, Detroit, and Minneapolis, half the land area of the cities is devoted to the movement and storage of automobiles. Roads, not counting parking facilities, now take up thirty percent of the land area in fifty-three central cities of the United States.

In urban environments like this, man is shackled to the car; there is no escape, no real alternative. One cannot readily walk. Distances are too great. Sidewalks are ornamental; they are not meant to be functional in cities built for automobiles. Bicycling can get you killed in cities built for automobiles. Rapid rail courses fixed, inflexible routes. If the trains are not close at hand, if they don't go your way when you want to go, it's back to the automobile. Buses don't accommodate the lifestyles of the huge middle class of Americans, those who do most of the driving.

Incredulous, I watch the lineup of automobiles at the entrance of the Chattahoochee National Recreational Area any nice day in Atlanta; patient people idling away in their cars, dressed in shorts, T-shirts, and running shoes, waiting *to go exercise*. I walk out of Cumberland Mall, a major regional shopping center on Atlanta's north side, and see the Galleria, another major shopping destination, not two hundred yards away. From one parking lot to the other I can throw a rock. But these two prime shopping destinations might as well be miles apart. A canyon separates them, a seven-lane, heavily traveled canyon of a thoroughfare that cannot be crossed without getting into the car and joining in the melee. It is no different in any other big U.S. city.

Roads for cars parcel up cities into stranded islands accessible only by car. Lunchtime in any modern big-city business district traditionally means a mad scramble for the parking lot and a thicket of congested roads as people "step out" for a bite to eat. They could walk to nearby restaurants and shops; many *would* walk, but the way is obstructed by traffic and it is dangerous. Did you ever watch a well-dressed businesswoman in high heels try to walk the irregular shoulder of a heavily traveled city street to meet someone for lunch? Ever see a couple of IBM types walking single file in the gutter, gravel, and broken glass with cars whizzing past their elbows? People *try to* live life on a human scale, but modern cities are designed for automobiles.

It doesn't have to be that way. There are transportation alternatives that can be effective, acceptable, and profitable. There are practical ways to move people that can free Western society from inordinate dependence on the gasoline-powered automobile, cut deeply into environmental degradation, stretch a precious natural resource far into the future, and reverse the fragmentation of big cities. The trick is to match available alternative transportation modes with the shape and requirements of the market, fitting the right pegs in the right holes, then to sell the solution.

Substantial accommodation for alternate transportation development would have to be made: rights-of-way; support systems for fuels, maintenance, and repair; creative financing; heroic levels of cooperation between government and private industry, to name just a few. Companies organized to introduce alternative transportation measures must be prepared to work the lawmaking apparatus with skill and vision. Communication capabilities must be of the highest order to develop a market following. It won't be easy, but the timing is good.

Virtually every major city suffers from intractable transportation and related pollution problems. The door is open for realistic solutions that have a decent chance of success. Show impacted governments where they can save money now spent on new roads, parking space, railline, buses, ground-level pollution abatement, storm-water management, and other costs of traffic congestion, and they can be induced to give back some of the savings to alternate transportation providers in the form of subsidies, rebates, feebates, or other types of compensation (see "Financing").

Above all, the public, the commuter, must buy into alternative transportation solutions. "We sell what customers buy," reminds a spokesman for the Association of International Automobile Manufacturers. If the public bought alternative transportation, things would change. People are concerned. They see the waste and perversion of transportation as usual. Offer them alternative transportation that is fun and fashionable—make it a novelty if need be—but make it effective and deliver it professionally, and the transition from lock-jaw reliance on the automobile will begin.

The alternative transportation forms to build businesses upon, the pegs to be fit into the right market niches, include pedestrian walkways, pedal-powered and pedal-assisted conveyances, electric cars, super-efficient low-polluting gasoline-powered vehicles, light rail and "bullet trains." The marketplace is virtually every big, congested metropolitan area.

Big cities sprawl around key commercial nodes or centers, pillars on which the entire megalopolis is built. In these nodes are grouped the key facilities and institutions that make a city a city—the major employers, the markets, the office space, hotels, factories, warehouses, and so on. In a city like Atlanta, that would be seven locations: Downtown, Midtown, Buckhead, the Cumberland-Galleria area, Perimeter Center, Northlake and the airport. Los Angeles has its unique collection of commercial nodes. So does Rome, Beijing, or New Delhi. Residentially, people live in different concentrations and track back and forth to the commercial nodes. Every big city is the same. Traffic, then, congeals in well-defined routes *between* work and home—that's the jammed expressway morning and evening—and *within* commercial centers—that's where parking facilities frequently cover more land than the buildings and where roads cut the city to pieces. Tremendous waste and pollution occur betwixt and between these nodes, and this is where the opportunities lie for alternate transportation businesses.

Let's look at some "easy" opportunities in a niche of alternative transportation that is generally overlooked.

PEDAL POWER

There is a hard core of U.S. bicycle commuters in our midst

that numbers at least 3.5 million, according to the Bicycle Institute of America. Twenty-three million adults sixteen years old or older bicycle at least once a week. Forget that little accommodation for bicycling is made in the United States. Some small markets provide for it, but, overall, bicyclists are left to run with the cars and trucks and fend for themselves. Still, several million Americans ply the roads between work and home on a bicycle. That is not an insignificant reduction in automotive pollution and clutter. Studies indicate that there is another sizable group of would-be commuters who would make the switch with just a little incentive—bicycling lanes and a place at work to shower and change are often cited.

The combined market, those who *do* bicycle commute and those who *would*, is substantial; yet no one caters to it, no one looks beyond municipal infrastructure improvements to get more people on bicycles and out of cars. It is not *just* the lack of bicycle lanes and dressing rooms that keeps people from using the bicycle as serious alternate transportation. There are other easy-to-address reasons that, corrected, can make bicycle commuting much more appealing. Keep in mind that the U.S. industry for bicycles and related parts and accessories in 1990 rang up receipts of $3.1 billion, so building off this base is not a bad beginning point.

FASHION

One prime reason people don't bicycle to work is clothing. It's tough to keep your Brooks Brothers suit or Saks careerwoman ensemble looking snappy after a three-to-six-mile bicycle commute on a hot day, and you sure can't wear typical bicycling attire into a normal place of work. By any standard, it is garish, outlandish. The colors are neon and loud and not always complementary; the fit is tight and dis-

tracting. Shoes are often stiff mechanical extensions of bicycle pedals that are not much good for simply walking.
Helmets top off the "look" with fins and swoops and lou-
vers that give the wearer the air of a mutant praying man-
tis. The clothing is functional—to a point. The advanced fabrics accommodate sweaty bodies very well, but little things—
like pockets—are not provided. In short, modern bicycle apparel came right off the European bicycle racing circuit and right
onto the streets of America and much of the rest of the
world. It works fine with the *peloton* grinding down the
Champs-Elysées, but it is not acceptable in the halls of IBM
or the local law office or on the factory floor at Westinghouse.

Bicycling attire doesn't have to be designed this way; it's
just that no one has considered the needs of the bicycle commuter market. What's needed is a selection of "pin-striped"
bicycle commuting clothes, garments that provide for the physical exertion of bicycling but blend in with the ambience of
the workplace, whether that be the executive suite or the factory floor. Such apparel may be akin to the stylish cuts of
CraZee Wear, the latest sportswear rage that couples loose-
fitting pants with subtle, quasi-elegant patterns. Some sort
of lapeled jacket reminiscent of a suit or sport coat would
be required. The bicycling equivalent of a "white business
shirt" should not be hard to fashion from today's high-
tech fabrics. Same for ties. Helmets can come in subtler
colors and styles; they could even contain the speaker-
receiver apparatus of a portable cellular telephone. No reason not to stay in touch just because you are on a bicycle.
Intelligent bicycle commuting apparel is purely a design and
marketing consideration. There is nothing to prevent a
firm from getting into the business but consumer acceptance.
CraZee pants and similar sportswear have been remarkably

successful because they combine style, versatility, and functionality. Bring those features to bicycle commuting apparel, and you tap into a potentially lucrative new market.

What businessman or woman can function without a briefcase that accommodates fat legal files, a calculator or two, a Day-Timer and wallet, and miscellaneous other tools of the trade? Increasingly, people lug around laptop computers and portable telephones. Women have purses. Bicycle luggage simply doesn't accommodate this very rudimentary, very typical fact of workaday life. There are long-distance bicycle touring panniers, cute little tool and handlebar bags, fanny packs, insulated compartments to keep a six-pack cold, impractical attaches to hold a pad of paper, but nothing to make it quick and easy for a working stiff to get his "stuff" back and forth to work. It is a hassle to load a bicycle with a variety of packs, a lock, tire pump, tool kit, and assorted clips and bungee cords. You have to remember the keys to the bike lock, keys to the house, the helmet, gloves, raingear. Once you get to work, everything has to come off so it doesn't get stolen. That can mean an armload of equipment that doesn't show well on the elevator ride to the twentieth floor. Then you have to go through the whole routine again at the end of the day. All in all, it's easier just to throw your stuff on the front seat of the car and forget the bicycle. But if someone developed an effective "executive bicycle commuter pak" that simplified the process of loading and unloading a commuter bicycle *and* looked professional on the conference room table, the market would jump at it. The unit would have to be a one-piece ensemble that clipped onto a rear bike rack quickly and securely and just as quickly came off. Locking and unlocking would need to be quick and easy. Laptop computers and/or cellular telephone compartments would need to be padded. . . .

There are 8,000 bicycle shops in the United States that ought to have "bicycle commuter departments" to carry apparel suitable for bicycling *and* the workplace, "executive commuter paks," appropriate commuter bicycles, locks, helmets, rain gear, bicycle telephones, portable computers—the whole package including route information and news on the subject. (How about a *Bicycle Commuter* magazine?) Someone might put together the package and franchise or license it to bicycle dealers. The opportunities here are truly international in scope. In fact, the market is larger in places like Europe and Japan where bicycle commuting is much more prevalent than in the United States. The possibilities need only to be explored. It should not be a hard sell to get funding assistance and other support from bicycle manufacturers and accessory makers for well-planned bicycle commuting ventures.

BICYCLE PARKING

Bicycle parking facilities are another glaring oversight on business's part. At the least, locking one's $500 to $1,000 bicycle to the nearest lamppost, handrail, or potted tree is inconvenient and a deterrence to cycling in lieu of driving; at the worst, it is a good way to lose the equipment or easy-to-use parts of it. In Japan and the Netherlands, where bicycle commuting is a major mode of transportation, "parking" bicycles is accommodated with the same business acumen as parking cars. And there is this to know about parking lots: commercial car parking operations, on a per-square-foot basis, are one of the most profitable forms of real estate development. As many as 110 cars per acre of parking surface earning $5 to $10 per day multiplied by most days of the year is a lot of cash flow for a low-overhead operation and a facility that is primarily asphalt, concrete, and white lines.

Twelve bicycles can be parked in a typical automobile parking space. Modern decked bicycle parking garages in Japan can handle thousands of units a day, and the whole complex can fit on a parcel of land not much bigger than a hamburger restaurant. The garage attendant walks the decks, guarding the equipment. Development cost for covered and guarded bicycle parking at eighty rail stations in the Netherlands is $64 per space, including operations, maintenance, labor, and profit margin. Maintenance and operating costs alone run $150 per space or more for the typical *unattended* auto park-and-ride lot. It's $4,000 per space to build a car parking lot, $50 to $500 per space for a guarded, covered, enclosed bicycle lot. Daily parking rates for bicycles are cheaper than for cars but, on a per-square-foot basis, revenues are actually higher while construction costs are lower. Pretty good economics, all in all. Bicycle lockers leased long term and coin-operated "bike racks" at low-volume sites make good sense but they have a mixed history of success. In the United States, in particular, vandalism and poor design restrict their widespread adoption. Design corrections and volume distribution could make this a profitable segment of the bicycle parking business.

Bicycle parking garages in congested business districts (commercial nodes) and at mass transit stations would be well received in many U.S. markets. Mass transit systems across the country continually struggle for ridership. More than 24 million workers live within two miles of a bus line or commuter rail of some sort. Yet transit authorities do nothing to make it easier for people to hop on a bicycle and "bike & ride" the local transportation system. Instead, many of these potential customers jump in a car and drive to work, right past the underutilized transit system. Everyone loses. In Japan, the reigning economic miracle among nations, there are 8,600 bicycle parking lots. In the Netherlands, whose standard of living ranks appreciably above that of the United States, there are thousands of bicycle parking lots. Bicycle parking lots in the United States? A handful, at most.

Bicycle parking lots should not be left to government to implement and the taxpayer to fund. The entrepreneur needs to develop the business plans, do the design work and market studies, arrange the financing, and go to the marketplace with a "salable, doable" package. The developer-operator should be able to trade off ridership gains by the transit system for subsidies or concessions to bolster income. Maybe the transit authority could contribute a deck site on a corner of the station grounds or pay as a subsidy a piece of each fare brought to the system by the "bike & ride." Similar trade-offs might be negotiated with building owners who could be spared the expense of adding costly automobile parking space, with major employers who pay the bill for employee parking, and with city officials who are compelled to spend and spend to move and store automobiles. An alternate transportation company well schooled in the principles of emission reduction credits (see "Financing") could make a convincing case for such "partners" to invest in bicycle parking accommodations.

There is no suggestion here that America or any other automobile-based society can be switched to bicycle commuting *en masse*, but the market can be cultivated much more effectively than has been done heretofore. Every bicycle on the road is pollution abated. It has been estimated that every commuter switched from a car to a bicycle saves 407 gallons of gasoline per year; that's 7,936 pounds of carbon dioxide that would not befoul man's habitat.

The avowed non-bicycle rider should be among the staunchest supporters of anything that will further bicycle use. Not everyone can escape the car, but everyone can make way for a machine that benefits us all. Make bicycle commuting "hot," give it fashion and consumer appeal and practicality, and it could make a difference. Combined with other forms of alternate transportation, it could begin the unbuckling of Western man's inordinate reliance on the automobile.

If bicycle commuting became fashionable—a trend—the political environment to push infrastructure changes would firm up dramatically. Dedicated bicycle lanes or paths would show up where before none seemed possible. Showers and dressing rooms would find their way into office buildings and other workplaces. The way would be opened for companies to specialize in pedestrian movement, simple developments that can maximize the ability of people to "commute" by foot where practical. Research shows that, up to half a mile, unobstructed walking is the *fastest* and most energy-efficient mode of transportation in urban areas, yet little is done to get the most out of this form of travel. A company formed to analyze, design, and develop pedestrian traffic networks in major markets could fill a valuable niche in the overall scheme of metropolitan traffic flow. A little thing like pedestrian direction signs to key destinations in a big convention town would make getting around a lot easier and a lot less polluting. An attractive sign in front of the hotel pointing the way to the nearby convention center or trade mart would get you going. A shady corridor of tree planters would draw you along. Benches for a rest stop would add to the ambience. Venues for small shopping kiosks or carts could be designed in; rents for the "retail space" could add substantially to company revenue. Emission reduction credit trade-offs with the city, property owners, and merchants would provide the principal remuneration (see "Financing").

The proposed firm would construct sidewalks where required; install planters, benches, and other ornamental devices; design and install directional signs; manage and lease the retail kiosks; build bus-stop shelters with secure bicycle parking accommodations (earning money from advertising on the shelters and coin-operated bike lockers); and promote and market the entire pedestrian network. Additional services might include the design of transportation management programs for small businesses and bicycle fleet management services for courier companies, police departments, delivery services, and so on. As we shall see later, the possibilities are extensive for an expanded "linchpin" organization of this type to tie together and maximize the efficiencies of all forms of alternate transportation.

How far can the concept of pedestrian transport be taken in automobile-bound societies? Perhaps further than might be thought with good planning and marketing and new twists on old modes of transportation.

Bombay, a teeming Asian city of ten million, moves people around town more efficiently than any major urban area. It's done with a motorized rickshaw, a glorified gasoline-powered golf cart. Step out of any hotel or office building or restaurant in any commercial center anywhere in town, and available to you with no wait or inconvenience is a sea of rickshaws manned by eager drivers ready to whisk you off to the front door of any destination in a two- or three-mile radius. Step right in: the cost is minimal, the seating is adequate, you are sheltered from the wind and elements with snap-on flaps, and the delivery time is unmatched by any other form of mass transit anywhere. Automobiles are not forbidden on city streets but they defer to the rickshaws, go at the rickshaws' pace. Cabs operate just outside the rickshaw zone and have their customers delivered to them by rickshaw.

China will forgo an automobile age altogether—too expensive for a poor, frugal country. Instead, this burgeoning, sprawling nation of 1.1 billion people gets by just fine on mass transit systems and the bicycle, mostly the latter. Jogging through many of China's cities in 1981, I was astonished by what can be done with a bicycle. Farmers passed me with five feet of hay mounded over the back of their sturdy two-wheelers. Two live pigs of thirty or so pounds each, tied down on their sides on a wooden slat, grunted at me as their owner pedaled by on business at the local market. A guy hauling a sofa, children perched between Daddy's outstretched arms, old people coming along gently—the whole society moves on the power of human legs. And it works.

PEDICABS

Can this kind of mobility—the rickshaw, brought to a higher level of technology, adapted to the reality of the marketplace—find acceptance in Houston or Los Angeles? Why not? If you stepped out of your midtown office building or suburban shopping mall and awaiting you was a clutch of attractive, high-tech, battery- or motor-assisted rickshaws manned by eager drivers, would you not take one if it were going your way and the fare was reasonable? People in America may not *straddle* bicycles in great profusion, but with the right marketing and packaging, lots of people might be induced to *sit in* a conveyance powered or principally powered by pedal. With variations, pedal-powered public conveyance shows its potential and consumer acceptance in operations around the country. With a comprehensive network of bicycle paths, the resort town of Hilton Head, South Carolina, sees heavy traffic in rental buggies that provide padded bench seats for two to four passengers, a fringed canopy against the sun, a quaint Model-T look and pedals at each seat. Theme parks like Sea World and Cypress Gardens provide pedicab service for their visitors that is heavily used. Commercial pedicab services of varying degrees of effectiveness contribute to public transportation in San Francisco, Los Angeles; Honolulu; New Orleans; Key West, Florida; Charleston, South Carolina; and other large pedestrian enclaves.

To get this mode of transportation out on the busy streets of the congested commercial nodes of America would take all the skills of a first-class business devoted solely to the purpose. If the service catches on in one market niche, the advantage is gained in all markets via franchising, licensing agreement, or other conventional methods of business expansion. Thus could economies of scale be achieved in the design and manufacture of equipment and operating overhead. Special tax districts would need to be established to provide subsidies to the pedicab operator so that revenue is attractive enough to warrant the risk of the venture. Every "fare" dropped into a cab's coinbox might get a matching amount from the levies of the tax district. Those businesses, employers, merchants, and governments that gain financially from improved traffic flow and savings in automobile accommodations and environmental cleanup can be shown the wisdom of setting aside a few mills of their savings for effective alternate transportation.

MASS TRANSIT

The economics and complexities of *fixed-rail* mass transit raise the risk factor of this proven form of alternate transportation to heights that deter all but the very largest from pursuing. Still, the environmental need for mass transit is too great (seventy percent of man-made air pollution is derived from transportation), the market is too promising, and the technology too functional for the business to be left to a handful of corporate behemoths and the glacial actions of public works. A single railroad can carry as many people as a ten-lane expressway. One magnetic levitation line (maglev) can move as many people as a six-lane expressway or major airport. Across a big city there is no mode of transport that can move more people faster or cheaper per passenger with less pollution than a super-high-speed train. Between regional cities—Atlanta and Birmingham, Tampa and Orlando, Anaheim and Las Vegas—not even air travel can compete with the speed of a "bullet train."

The technologies are proven; feasibility and user acceptance are no longer an issue. The people of Japan and France reap the many benefits of rail travel at 200 miles per hour. Ontario, Canada's 180-mph GO train is one of the best-planned and most successful commuter services in the world. Though very secretive about passenger volumes and other details relating to its theme-park monorails, the Walt Disney organization is clearly very pleased with the mode of transportation. The Morgantown, West Virginia, Automated People Mover (APM) has been a model of intelligent alternative transportation since its development in 1975. Vancouver has its Skytrain; Detroit, Miami, Jacksonville, and

Las Vegas their Downtown People Movers (DPM).

Japan and Germany have produced full-scale passenger-carrying maglev prototypes that operate in excess of 250 mph (321 mph is the current speed record). Magnetic fields lift, guide, and propel maglev vehicles over an elevated guideway. Because the train literally "floats" on a magnetic field, the ride is quiet and soft; speed is limited principally by air resistance. The Japanese aim for a 1994 opening of their first revenue-generating maglev line in Hokkiso, which will run from Sapporo the airport. The German Transrapid maglev system has operated on a twenty-mile test track for several years. A full-fledged commercial route is scheduled to commence operations in 1997, connecting Düsseldorf and Cologne airports in the first link of a 62-mile line between Essen and Bonn. Proposals have been made to upgrade this plan to a 640-mile system from Hamburg in the north to Munich in the south. With stops in key cities, the trip start to finish would take three and a half hours.

The Florida High Speed Rail Corporation has announced plans to develop a bullet train between Orlando and Tampa, a distance of eighty miles. The California-Nevada Super Speed Ground Transportation Commission has issued formal requests for proposals to build and operate a $3.5 billion high-speed rail line between Las Vegas and Anaheim in southern California, a distance of 265 miles. A joint venture of Bechtel Engineering and Germany's Transrapid International has proposed a maglev system that would cover the distance in one hour. Amtrak currently takes seven and a half hours.

Other major players have responded to the request for proposals with competing schemes. Senator Daniel Moynihan (D-New York) has taken the lead in pushing the U.S. government to develop a national maglev transportation system that would run along the interstate highway system. The entire European continent is laying cooperative plans for a massive high-speed train network that will stretch from Scotland and Scandinavia in the north to Spain in the west to Italy and Greece in the south and east. The 19,000-mile system is expected to cost $100 billion and take twenty-five years to complete. Trains would travel up to 185 mph. The trip from England to France *under* the English Channel is expected to be a thirty-minute excursion.

These developments and many others on the drawing board are exciting, but the future of fixed-rail mass transportation in its many forms is far from clear, particularly in the United States. With costs of $10 million to $67 million *per mile* of rail and operating revenues controlled by politics instead of the marketplace, few see any way to make money in the business. But the field may be opening up on the light-rail end of the spectrum. Where property owners, merchants, and employers can be sold on the financial benefits of a transit system that saves them money in automobile accommodations and feeds their businesses with large volumes of customers, and where local governments will trade reductions in traffic congestion, pollution, and roadway expenses for a lesser payout of tax subsidies, light rail transit systems make good business sense. The Florida "bullet train" planned to link Miami, Orlando, and Tampa was conceived as a pure business venture in which the investors would recoup their costs and earn a profit in real estate developments at key transit stations along the route. The 1990-92 recession and real estate collapse changed the deal to include some state tax support, but the original plan remains the strength of the project. Las Colinas, a mixed-use planned community near Dallas, Texas, was designed and developed with sections of guideway and stations in place even though the transit system had not been decided upon. A 16,500-foot first-phase Automated People Mover and four stations have since been constructed. Sites have been identified for an additional five stations as future parcels of the vast project are developed.

Architect Peter Calthorpe makes extensive use of light rail in his award-winning "Pedestrian Pockets" approach to real estate development. Calthorpe defines Pedestrian Pockets as "a balanced, mixed-use area within a quarter of a mile walking radius of a transit station which mixes auto, rail and pedestrian access to home and work. The goal is to create an environment in which the convenience of the car and the opportunity to walk would be blended; in which the economic engine of new growth, the back office, would be balanced with affordable housing and retail service. These pockets would be implanted into an existing suburban fabric by the creation of light rail lines and a clustering of new development at each of its stations. The [developed venues] are small, from fifty to a hundred acres, but the whole system accommodates projected growth with minimal impact; less land consumed, less traffic generated, less pollution produced."

Calthorpe gets to the crux of the benefits of light rail; it pays off in real money in a lot of ways. By providing an effective alternative to the automobile, the developer can service his property with less roadway and parking space, thus reducing those expenses plus the acreage requirements of the total project. More revenue-generating facilities (homes, offices, retail space) can be built on less land without exceeding density restrictions or sacrificing open spaces. Merchant transactions lost to traffic congestion are reduced, the conduct of business is facilitated with the ease of mobility, and residential life is enhanced by the easy proximity to work and play . . . All are very salable benefits to a discriminating market. Fewer cars and less land covered in roads and parking surfaces means less storm-water management infrastructure and related expenses. The cost of complying with clean air standards is diminished.

ALTERNATIVE AUTOMOBILES

Electric cars are legitimate alternative transportation with a big future. But they are not necessarily pollution free as generally advertised. There is no *exhaust pipe* emission from electric cars; the pollution occurs back at the power plant that generates the electricity that charges the car's batteries. In fact, vehicles that use electricity derived from the current mix of power sources in the United States would release about the same amount of carbon dioxide as gasoline-fueled cars, more sulfur dioxide, but much lower levels of other pollutants. Electric vehicles running solely on coal-produced electricity would substantially exceed the carbon dioxide emissions released by a typical gasoline-powered car. When the electricity is generated by gas-fired power plants, however, electric cars can reduce automotive emissions of hydrocarbons by 98.8 percent, carbon monoxide by 99.7 percent, nitrogen oxides by 83.6 percent, sulfur oxides by 98 percent and particulates by 4.8 percent, say researchers at the University of California–Davis. Solar-generated electricity would cut those emissions to zero. So, pick the right fuel and electric cars *can* be pollution free.

On the road, battery-stored electric power cannot compete nose to nose with the internal combustion engine, but it doesn't have to. Electric cars only have to fill a niche in an overall multimodal transportation scheme to be quite valuable both as a tool in the fight against environmental degradation and as a business venture. The Dutch probably come the closest to a working illustration of what a multimodal transportation system should look like. The most bicycle-friendly of all industrialized countries, the Netherlands has the world's highest density of both cycleways and automobiles plus a top-flight public transit system. Bicycles, walkways, rail service, and the automobile—each one fits into an overall scheme that maximizes its advantages and compensates for its deficiencies. The combined effect of this multimodal network is a transportation system that moves more people more efficiently with less environmental degradation than any other industrialized society. Into this network has been added the electric car. Commuters in Amsterdam drive in to rail stations from nearby residential communities and park in designated parking spaces that provide electric cords. Plug in the car, catch the train to work and, while they're logging their "9 to 5," the car is recharged for the trip back home in the evening.

Running in the fast lane—even the slow lane—of America's big-city expressways is not a very realistic utilization of electric cars given their current state of development. There is no support system of service stations in place for the electric car as there is for the gasoline-powered car; battery technology is simply not going to make the electric car the workhorse that is a gasoline-powered car. But if used to ply back and forth from home to work or a transit station, where there are recharging accommodations at each end of the line, the electric car can cut heavily into ground-level accumulations of hydrocarbons, ozone, carbon dioxide buildup, and nitrogen and sulfur emissions.

It is these benefits that prompted California to require that at least two percent of new cars sold in the state by 1998 produce no exhaust emissions. The figure rises to ten percent by 2003. In car-happy California, that will be a tidy piece of business. Each of the Big Three U.S. automakers is hard at work developing products to capitalize on the opportunity. Fine-tune electric car technology in the tough environment of California, then take the product elsewhere. Can a significant national and worldwide market be far behind California? Revisions in the U.S. Clean Air Act of 1990 are forcing eighty cities to take stringent steps to curb pollution; sixty percent of it is caused by the conventional gasoline-powered automobile. Electric cars are a realistic way to reach compliance. In October 1991, nine eastern states and Washington, D.C., agreed to adapt California's far-reaching program to cut automobile-induced urban smog. The market potential for electric cars is very promising, the business opportunities varied and extensive.

RECHARGING STATIONS

Perhaps the biggest opportunity is in the support side of electric car utilization. The organization that specialized in battery recharging stations at transit points and key workplaces would be in an excellent position to become *the* "gas station" chain of the electric car industry. Develop electric car parking lots that provide electrical outlets for recharging the car's battery while the owner puts in his workday. Deliver the electricity from on-site solar- or wind-powered generators, and the cost of doing business is reduced and fossil fuel emissions attributable to the operation are eliminated altogether. Generate revenue from parking fees and, perhaps, the metered electricity sold. Design an electric car "support package" for conventional gasoline service stations and sell a retrofit service to bring them current with market requirements. Round out the service with natural gas "pumps" to accommodate the other alternatively fueled vehicles. Repair and maintenance services must be provided for electric cars. Clearly, this is an adjunct to the recharging stations. Ultimately they must be as ubiquitous as today's gasoline service station. Electric car rechargers and natural gas dispensing units for the home might make sense.

Electric car batteries are a dynamic field with many exciting developments converging on new generations of power supply that will propel vehicles longer, farther, faster, less expensively, and more reliably. Electric car battery distribution, sales, repair, reuse, and recycling are all promising business opportunities (see "Batteries"). As with all new technological developments, there is always the opportunity for the inventive to bring enhancements to the industry—better ways to air-condition so that less electricity goes to ancillary uses, battery advances, weight reduction.

While it would be tough to compete with the likes of General Motors, Ford, and Chrysler in the design and manufacture of electric cars, it is certainly not out of the question. After all, it was tiny Apple Computer that blew away some of the big boys like Sperry Rand and Honeywell in the early years of the personal computer industry. Swatch, the giant Swiss watchmaker, is a major factor in the manufacture of electric cars. The history of nearly all developing industries is marked by many early entries in the competition and plenty of dark-horse winners. A more feasible opportunity, however, is the advancement of electric car battery technology in other alternative forms of transportation, particularly pedal-assisted conveyances like pedicabs.

Sales is another opportunity in the electric car field.

General Motors expected to sell 500 electric vehicles in 1990. Ford and Chrysler are pushing their products. To promote the sale of electric cars in smog-ridden cities, U.S. Representative George Brown(D-California introduced a bill in 1990 that would provide a $50 million federal subsidy for five years to defray the cost of producing and acquiring the vehicles. At present, the cost of electric cars is estimated to be double the threshold of customer acceptance. Given the growing costs associated with the cleanup of pollution in many big cities, there is fertile ground here for the implementation of "feebate" programs or emission reduction credit trade-offs between electric car owners and local governments (see "Financing"). It would prove to be cheaper for local authorities to contribute in some manner to the cost of electric cars than to clean up the pollution left behind by gasoline-powered vehicles.

CAR DEALERSHIPS

A real possibility in alternative transportation is "environmental car dealerships." Bring together in one dealership program the full line of commercially ready electric vehicles, alternatively fueled vehicles (natural gas, methanol), and super-efficient gasoline-powered cars like the Mitsubishi Orion, the Geo Metro and the Honda Civic CRX HF. Any one of these vehicles would be little more than a novelty in a typical manufacturer's showroom full of conventional automobiles. Sales personnel would have no more incentive to sell a nonpolluting or low-polluting car than they would a gas hog. Manufacturers face the problem and expense of marketing an atypical product. Overall, acceptance by the marketplace might lag. But put these vehicles together under one roof, set up a marketing organization and sales staff tailored specifically and exclusively to sell them, and the cars would move. Package and franchise the business. Money would be made. The environment would be well served.

Then there is the potential for new *manufacturers* of environmentally sensitive gasoline-powered automobiles. Plastic bodies and new makes of engines open the door to new players on the world automotive scene. U.S. automakers are in full-scale decline, and as protectionist governmental policies increasingly stymie innovative imports, a "product gap" is sure to develop. Space-age plastics and composites can be pressed into large, complex body assemblies at costs that are significantly cheaper than conventional steel fabrication. There are new types of motors that can do the job more cheaply, more efficiently, with less pollution. The two-stroke Orbital engine developed in Australia is twenty-five percent more efficient than today's best four-cylinder engines and about twenty percent less expensive to produce. Traditional automakers are not the only ones who can put together these components to create a new line of American automobiles, not in today's business environment.

Let's get really wild. Every major metropolis in the United States and most Western countries is served by arterial expressway systems that tie suburbs with the city, and city with city. At crucial times—morning and evening rush hours—they also become vast parking lots, spewing hazardous waste, getting no one anywhere fast. Normal commuting time is a half hour to one and a half hours, unchanged from the days when people walked and drove horse-drawn wagons. What if today's expressways did their jobs a little differently? They were designed to get people from "A" to "B" faster. Between cities, they deliver on their promise; but as local transit, they fail. In close to town, there are just too many vehicles and not enough expressway, and without paving over the host city, enough expressway cannot be built.

What if the local expressway system was converted to a multimodal transport complex that included roadside parking for cars and bicycles, battery recharging stations for electric cars, a continuous-loop Automated People Mover (APM), plus the normal expressway lanes for through traffic? Drive or bicycle from home in the suburbs to the expressway feeder system, park the vehicle and catch the train to your exit; there ,grab a pedicab or connecting APM to work. Make the "modern" city work for people.

Obviously, the world is far from this presently, not because it can't be done, not because the consumer wouldn't buy it, but because no one shows the way, no one gathers the wherewithal and takes the lead in the serious business of metrowide multimodal transportation systems. Like everything else outside the realm of the familiar and habitual, a comprehensive, integrated mix of conventional and alternative forms of transportation has to be sold to the market and the goods delivered and operated as billed. The business organizations to accomplish this are not in place; they must form and go to work if man is to avoid driving himself into oblivion. Leave to the airplane those things it is singularly equipped to do—moving lots of people very long distances fast. High-speed rail and maglev service clearly makes sense for distances of 50 to 500 miles, so propose it, develop it, make it happen. Install light rail and APMs where they fit. Focus on the easy stuff first: maximize the flow of traffic by foot and pedal. Make this the beginning point of a sophisticated multimodal transportation network that includes a place for the private car, but a much more modest place than presently held.

Carpooling

Carpooling cannot be overlooked in the search for a way out of the automobile trap. California's fight to clean its air has raised carpooling to the rank of legitimate business venture. The South Coast Air Quality Management District's Regulation XV "has created a whole new market for consultants who can assist or advise companies that are required to develop ride-share plans," says spokeswoman Claudia Keith. As practiced in California, ride-sharing operations are the product of complex commuter pattern analyses; program design, implementation, and monitoring; environmental impact assessment; traffic engineering; parking design; psychology; corporate communications; and a host of other disciplines. California is not the end of the market for the ride-sharing business, it is but the beginning. Look for some corporate giants and personal fortunes to emerge from those firms cutting their teeth now in California carpooling.

The current cost of gasoline at the pump is cheap. It permits us tremendous indulgences. But the *true cost* of gasoline is astronomical. We cannot afford the atmospheric pollution it causes, the greenhouse warming it contributes to, the "cementification" and "asphaltification" it encourages, the city planning it brings, the lifestyles it creates. Alternative, nonpolluting modes of transportation are part of the solution. Where they can be brought into play, the atmosphere needs to be created for it to occur. But there are applications where there is no good substitute for petroleum-based liquid fuel. Where this is the case, use it, but use it superefficiently and *eliminate the discharge of pollutants,* whatever the cost. Big strides are being made in the reformulation of transportation fuels to reduce harmful emissions. Cars are now available that are four to five times more fuel efficient than the average fleet mileage. Catalytic converters, under optimum conditions, can cut roughly ninety percent of harmful exhaust emissions. But these advances do nothing to halt the rise in atmospheric pollution. The reason is simple: according to 1986 findings, 10,000 new drivers and 28,000 new cars are added to U.S. roads every twenty-four hours. An analysis by Washington University's Center for the Study of American Business reveals that an increase of forty percent in the average U.S. fleet mileage (the corporate average fuel economy, or CAFE) as proposed in Congress would decrease U.S. gasoline demand by less than one-fourth of one percent—not even a day's worth of gasoline consumption.

Alternative transportation fuels like natural gas, methanol, ethanol, and others are promoted by various interests, including the U.S. Department of Energy, as the logical complement and eventual successor to gasoline. But clean-burning they are not. Per unit of energy achieved, they discharge carbon dioxide at about the same rate as gasoline. Ethanol, an alcohol made principally from corn, reduces automotive lead and carbon monoxide emissions but offsets that with the production of four times the aldehyde emissions of gasoline. Aldehydes add to ground-level ozone formation and, unlike gasoline, damage plant life. Methanol emits formaldehyde, nasty stuff used in cadaver preservation. Loose talk has emerged about biofuels that create *no effective* carbon dioxide waste because the tree specifically cultivated to make the fuel takes in the same amount of carbon dioxide during its photosynthetic life as it emits when burned. That is a spurious claim in the real world of planetary deforestation. Tree coverage the size of the United States would need to be planted before the balancing act between carbon dioxide output and absorption could begin. Whatever the currently available transportation fuel, upon its combustion, hazardous waste is thrown into our midst. That is the critical flaw in conventional automotive transportation.

FOOL THINGS FOR SMART PEOPLE

Changing the way affluent populations get around could take a long time—perhaps too long—but there are steps that can be taken right now to speed the transition. At the will of the people, the price of gasoline could be hiked dramatically to curb demand and help with the cost of alternative transportation. "Green fees" could be tacked on to the price of a polluting gas hog (and rebates paid for low-polluting cars. Called "feebates," the rebate would be funded from penalties collected on the gas hogs). Automobile registration fees could be made expensive. Since many commuters drive to work because employers provide free parking, the amenity could be taxed at a rate high enough to be a deterrence. Toll booths could be placed on key thoroughfares to collect payment for their use. "Congestion fees" might be charged to vehicles with fewer than four passengers as they do in Singapore. For those who drive excessively, charge an "excessive drivers tax" as they do in the Netherlands.

Put back on the automobile driver the hidden expenses of driving: the cost of roads and their maintenance, the police and fire services required, the costs of accidents and health care—a figure estimated to be as much as $300 billion annually—and the unfathomable expense of environmental degradation. Let the individual make his or her decision on where and how much to drive, but make it a legitimate economic decision. Force people to seriously consider the cost of gasoline-powered mobility, and they will surprise with their creativity and priorities. Graduate the price hikes and levies selectively: the highest for inefficient private cars carrying one passenger, the lowest perhaps for transport of food and other basic commodities and for the elderly and the poor. Pool the revenue generated from the various changes in a separate fund to help finance the development and implementation of effective forms of alternate transportation and energy.

Why would the public do such a damn fool thing as voluntarily hike the cost of a critical necessity like transportation? Because it is emphatically in their individual best interests. Besides, the alternatives to traditional gasoline-powered mobility are not unattractive. We could still get back and forth to work for about the same cost and in about the same time, considering traffic delays. Oil companies would still make their money; highway departments and contractors have thousands of bridges and millions of miles of highway to maintain and adapt to new forms of transportation; and entire industries would spring up with all the economic benefits they bring. The grass roots movement called NIMBY ("not in my backyard") has been spectacularly successful in forcing changes in the business of waste disposal. No less a crusade is needed against the gasoline-powered automobile.

REAL ESTATE DEVELOPMENT

The transportation picture is not complete without addressing suburban sprawl. Before the automobile, cities grew from a central core. Municipal services worked efficiently because population densities and short distances kept costs low. People lived close enough to work to get there on foot or by other simple modes of transport. The remnants of these village environments can still be seen in London, Paris, New York City, San Francisco. It worked. It could work even better now because infrastructure technology and capabilities are far superior.

Modern suburban sprawl is anathema to man's limited habitat. It means continually stripping and covering the land on the outer margins of metro areas and leaving behind dead and useless inner cities; it means more roads and long-haul automobiles to get around; it means overextended utilities, services, and gargantuan infrastructures; it means a distorted scale that consumes too much and wastes too much. Willy-nilly suburban sprawl has to stop. "In-filling" and the "Pedestrian Pocket" concept espoused by architect Peter Calthorpe must become the norm. Give to modern "doughnut-towns" the vibrance that make cities exciting: population densities, a village scale, and all the things possible in such environments. Legislate against clearing and developing new land on the periphery of modern cities while there remains undeveloped or underdeveloped property in town. Dead inner cities will then become valuable development property. Donald Trump, real estate guru of the eighties, made much of his fortune tearing down existing New York City buildings and putting up new ones in their place. The Rouse Company of Columbia, Maryland, built its impressive reputation by putting back into major cities what used to be there—a heart, a central core of pedestrian-friendly amenities that bring people back to their roots.

Peter Calthorpe notes, "Our current round of suburban growth is generating a crisis of many facets: mounting traffic congestion, diminishing affordable housing, receding open space, and stressful social patterns. The truth is we are using planning strategies which are forty years old and relevant to a different culture; our household makeup has changed dramatically, the workplace and work force have been transformed, real wealth is shrinking, and environmental concerns have surfaced. But we are still building World War II suburbs as if families were large and had only one breadwinner, as if all the jobs were downtown, as if land and energy were endless, and as if another lane on the freeway would end traffic." Before the automobile, people lived in town, worked in town and entertained in town; twenty-four hours a day, the city worked for its creators. Today, major urban areas are mere eight-hour-a-day places of work; the other sixteen hours of the day are spent in the suburbs. The city's efficiency is lost in the suburban sprawl.

Telecommuting

There are services to be provided, and money to be made, that can lessen the detrimental effects of suburban sprawl. The growing capabilities of computers, telephones, fax machines, electronic mail, and other telecommunications devices make it increasingly attractive for employers to let employees work at home and in satellite communities well removed from the "office." Not only is the technology available to telecommute effectively, the trend in office space usage is to drastic downsizing.

"Major firms want to know how to reduce overhead, improve operations, and increase employee productivity," explained Mahlon "Sandy" Apgar IV at a recent Washington, D.C., conference on corporate office trends. "And the facts of office occupancy cost in virtually every company office in America are similar. . . . For many, the cost per square foot per employee has doubled in the 1980s." Office space requirements must be reduced if firms are to improve profitability. "Current costs per person must be halved," said Cesar Chekijian, corporate vice president of real estate at New York's Manufacturers Hanover Trust Company. "It has to get back to where it was in the sixties and seventies."

A fledgling telecommuting industry could not ask for a better business environment in which to take flight. Every company employee who can work at home effectively means 150 to 400 square feet of expensive office space and related fixtures and support the employer can do without. Time wasted commuting back and forth to work becomes productive time when an employee works at home. Every employee who "commutes" from the upstairs bedroom to the downstairs office is one less automobile lurching along the expressway. Telecommuting is an excellent substitute for automobile commuting.

IBM, Hayes Microcomputers, and other major firms experiment with the idea. In San Diego, roughly ten percent of the 900 county public works department employees "telecommute" one to three days per week. Plans are in place to build several satellite centers in outlying areas, complete with fax machines and other equipment, to enhance the process. A former staff assistant at the Jimmy Carter Presidential Center in Atlanta provides typing services for lawyers and other clients from his office at home. Clients call and dictate their work into a recorder (they could fax a rough copy if need be). Edward White transcribes the work and sends it back to the customer's computer via computer modem. If he gets buried with work, he can farm out some of it over the telephone to other typists *anywhere* who have an accommodating computer and modem. The U.S. Census Bureau in a 1989 survey found two million Americans who used computers to work at home. A more recent estimate puts the figure at more than five million, a number that is expected to double by 1995.

Is there a good *Home Office* magazine for the millions of employees and self-employed who now work at home? Who would design and install the necessary paraphernalia and network for effective telecommuting? Who would sell the concept and the system to employers and employees? Who would develop programs for small towns to attract "new industry" without bringing in the factory? Might communities develop strategies and incentives to attract *just* telecommuters? Might there be emission reduction trade-offs with city governments that would create income to help offset the costs of telecommuting equipment and related expenses?

CHAPTER TEN

SOLAR & OTHER ALTERNATIVE FORMS OF ENERGY

Enough solar energy falls on the United States every day to provide the society's energy needs for eighteen months. To be used by man, the sunlight needs only to be converted from its diffused state to concentrated form (solar thermal) or directly to electricity (photovoltaics) and brought to the marketplace. That, of course, is a great leap in technology and marketing skills. But in 1992, the solar technology exists to provide as much as eighty percent of building heating, cooling, and lighting needs. Small motors and giant turbines can be driven by the sun. What's missing is the marketing.

Solar energy development over the last twenty-five years has been channeled in two directions, both of them wrong. Solar, it is said by the energy establishment, is for the *fringe* of the market, those applications where it is economically unwise to run power lines: remote cabins, vacation homes, and the like. Then there are the ongoing efforts to tie solar energy into the industrial world's great electric power distribution grid; that is the weakest of solar's many applications. On the strength of funding provided by the electric power industry and the federal government, the United States leads the world in solar science and technology, but far too much of it is devoted to bending solar energy to the special interests of its benefactors. Electric utilities don't really want solar except as an adjunct to what they already do; it has been forced on them by law (PURPA, the Public Utility Regulatory Policies Act of 1978), and one suspects that the principal purpose of the *ongoing* solar research funded by the electric power industry is to keep it *ongoing* and out of the marketplace.

Keep the public quiet with the electric power industry's obvious commitment to solar technology, give the market fringes to the "solar guys," but keep them out of the lucrative core of the marketplace—suburbia, commercial buildings, industry. The real market for solar energy is the same market targeted and controlled by the electric power industry. Until and unless it is developed for the mass market, including especially mainstream suburbia anywhere in the industrialized world, solar energy will be a very long time ever approaching its potential and all societies will pay dearly.

Mankind *needs* solar to ascend and fossil fuel consumption to descend. Solar produces energy on a direct one-to-one ratio: solar energy in equals energy out with no pollution left over. Three parts fossil fuel goes into making one part electrical energy; two parts are left as pollution. We cannot long continue with those ratios. Conventional electric power generation need not, cannot, be supplanted anymore than gasoline-powered transportation, but it needs to be reined in, subjugated instead of subjugating. Actually, the electric power industry can win coming and going: if forced by widespread market adoption of solar energy, the industry can adapt quickly to collect and distribute solar-generated electricity in lieu of, or in conjunction with, conventionally produced current. Storage capabilities would have to be perfected to "bank" solar energy while the sun's out for use when it isn't; technologies to "level" the variable nature of sunlight are not advanced enough to prevent giant turbines from surging and slowing. But the electric power industry explores these technologies; spurred by growing solar usage, the capabilities would come much more quickly than might be imagined. It is not inconceivable that the electric power industry could become the *conduit* for independently produced power as much as the *producer* of electrical energy.

Because of the power-plant focus of its technology and because the lead is in science and technology and not in *utilization*, the United States runs the risk of losing its dominance in the solar energy field. Sixty percent of the country's thermal solar products are sold abroad and eighty percent of its photovoltaic units. India and Brazil are big buyers. Switzerland has made a major commitment to solar. Nuclear power has been ruled out by the nation's voters. Hydroelectric dams, a big energy contributor in this alpine region, will be built no more. "I expect to see three kilowatts of solar energy panels on every rooftop in Switzerland," said one leading U.S. utility consultant. "In the 1980s the U.S. market for solar technology dried up," explained Scott Sklar, executive director of the Solar Energy Industries Association. "The only way to survive was to export. . . . My fear is that in the next five to six years, this industry will be a foreign industry." Maverick entrepreneur John Strode got tired of "screwing around with the utilities and the government" and forged ahead on private bank funding with Armech Solar Power, Inc., the largest solar panel manufacturing facility in the world. "I can sell everything I can make," he said, dismissing the establishment view that solar is still experimental.

The solar energy business needs to step out of the shadow of the electric power industry. By going its own way, solar can drive events in the electric power industry instead of the other way around. Those who will make fortunes in solar energy are those who will go after the market with either "stand-alone" products that deliver their utility independent of the electric power grid or products that are *supplemented* by conventional electricity.

PHOTOVOLTAICS

Photovoltaics (PV), a brilliant technology that converts sunlight directly into electricity, has a broad range of applications that, rolled into a comprehensive business plan, could result in a major marketing coup. Ironically, the immediate opportunity in PV lies in that fringe area of the greater energy market long consigned to solar energy—remote odds-and-ends places where it is too expensive or impossible to string a power line. The difference today is that the business potential is much more extensive than remote cabins and vacation homes, and some of the business no longer looks so unappealing to the electric power industry.

Bridge lights, for example, can be powered quite handily by batteries charged during the day by small PV units. Costs compared with utility wiring, conduit, switching equipment, and electric bills are lower, and no pollution accrues to the expense of mankind. Expressway sign lighting is the same application as bridge lighting. Billboards too. Buoy lights in the world's sea lanes and security fence lights and warning systems are other applications. Line-breakers on the electric power grid system of North America, Europe, and elsewhere still must be reengaged by hand after a power surge. A remote PV unit at each line-breaker could enable the job to be done electronically rather than dispatching an employee to the boonies to do it. Add to these uses the ability of PV or solar thermal devices to power irrigation pumps, grind grain, and treat wastewater where there is no power grid, and the market potential gets impressive. The U.S. Department of Energy has identified no fewer than fifteen PV applications with investment paybacks of less than one year.

The power companies see the potential for stand-alone solar energy; look for them to begin to build small modular PV units to service the demand. Power company managers are smart guys. They see nothing wrong with solar so long as it is controlled by the utility. But there is nothing to prevent private PV companies from getting to the market first and finally breaking the public utility's monopolistic hold on a huge slice of the energy business. All that's needed is recognition of the market and an organization to capture a share of it. With no consideration given to most of the applications noted above, the market for PV systems is projected to top $1 billion by the end of the century.

SOLAR APPLIANCES

Light sensors already monitor the daylighting (sunlight) in some modern office space and add in just enough man-made lighting (light bulbs) to keep overall illumination at constant optimal levels. When the sun is bright and lighting is good, electricity use is eliminated; when clouds gather, enough electricity is brought in to make up the lighting shortfall. This capability opens the way for solar "roof shingles" or a high-tech "solar appliance." Sanyo Corporation makes a solar roof shingle that can meet all the lighting needs of the average house. Texas Instruments in concert with Southern California Edison is closing in on an even better model.

Upper-middle-class suburbia is not going to clutter up its

expensive rooftops with horsey conventional solar collectors, but it can be sold on the merits of a shingle look-alike that doubles as a nonpolluting power source and pays for itself and then some in electricity savings and co-generation sales. At peak daylight hours on sunny days in sunny climes, such a roof can provide all the energy needed to run a home or many commercial buildings. Any overage must be taken back by the power company under present law as co-generated electricity, an income maker. Where the solar energy falls short—cloudy days, nights—light sensors can bleed in just enough electricity from the power grid to even things out. Do this in home after home, subdivision after sub-division and things will begin to change in the energy busi-ness. Put on a push to develop on-site battery storage of solar energy for use at night, pull the whole system together in a neat package and market it with the verve and sophistica-tion of a new line of computers, and solar energy will begin to move, fossil fuel consumption will begin to ebb.

In the establishment's ongoing search for solar systems to provide utility-scale electricity, stand-alone devices for a single home or business have gone wanting. What if the best in solar technology were rolled into a sophisticated, space-age, aesthetically pleasing *appliance* that fit as neatly in the residential landscape as the ubiquitous air conditioner or TV antenna dish? What if it were taken out of the novelty cat-egory and brought into the mainstream of home ownership, not necessarily as a *replacement* for traditional electric power but as a *supplement?* What if it were pushed and marketed on the strength of its *utility* and *cost-effectiveness* just like refrig-erators, washers and dryers, or any other household "neces-sity"? Would it not sell? Would it not become *acceptable?* Could it not become the new status symbol that everyone in the neighborhood had to have; a svelte, humming proclamation that "I, the owner, see the future and I am responding"?

The Sterling Engine is a good candidate for the "suburban solar appliance." It concentrates sunlight with a parabolic dish onto a liquid that produces temperatures as high as 5,000 degrees. The heat then powers a generator to produce electricity. The Sterling Engine's promise is among the most exciting in the solar industry, but it is targeted to industrial uses. Miniaturized, this technology, coupled with battery storage for off-hours, might well become every man's power plant.

The market for such an appliance is huge: every home in every subdivision in the industrialized world *and* every hovel in the Third World. Refined in suburbia, imbued with the economies of assembly-line production and produced in an "economy model," the suburban solar appliance could be a godsend to every poor wretch struggling day to day for enough fuel to cook, heat, and light. Such a unit—portable, easily installed, self-contained, driven by the sun—could handily supply the energy needs of several households at a time in any impoverished area. Host governments and, perhaps, private relief organizations could fund the front-end costs of the equipment (see "Financing"). There is no hope that deforestation, soil loss, desertification, and atmospheric alteration will end or even slow down as long as so much of mankind must scour his habitat daily for the minimal fuels of life. All of us are imperiled as long as this condition persists.

The solar energy business is not without excellent industrial markets. A German firm, Luz International, developed the nine largest solar electricity generating plants in the world in California's Mojave Desert. Operated by three separate owners, the plants sell their power output to Southern

California Edison. The Luz technology, sold recently to the Israeli government, employs fields of parabolic trough collectors that generate enough heat to power conventional turbines.

Acres upon acres of glistening solar collectors are not a very appealing prospect to many people; trading off air pollution for "solar collector pollution" is not fully satisfying. But there are compensating balances in the approach taken by Luz. First, it uses terrain that is of no other use to mankind. Deserts could well become the solar energy factories of the world and take from man none of his habitat. Secondly, solar collection devices will get smaller and deliver more energy per square foot of surface area, so less land coverage will be required to produce the same amount of electricity produced today. Thirdly, solar-generated electricity is fast approaching the retail kilowatt price of conventional electricity (about six cents per kilowatt-hour). On a full-cost-pricing basis—adding in the cost of environmental degradation and cleanup—solar is far cheaper than conventional electricity whether derived from fossil or nuclear fuels. It is this point that speaks most eloquently for the pursuit of solar energy.

A firm in Denver, Colorado, builds solar energy plants for prisons and other institutions, providing all the hot water and space heating required by the facilities. Other candidates for stand-alone solar water and space heating systems include bakeries, meat packing plants, canneries, schools, and grocery stores. Water heating and space heating consume thirteen percent of all energy generated in the United States, a massive expenditure of fossil fuel that piles on the pollution. The average residential hot-water heater uses as much energy as a car. The South Coast Air Quality Management District found that nothing except carpooling eliminated more ground-level ozone pollution than solar water heaters. Add in space cooling—air-conditioning—and the percentage of total U.S. energy consumed for heating water and "conditioning" space climbs past thirty percent. In short, water heating and space heating and cooling is a tremendous market that can be readily serviced by modern solar technology at costs that are substantially below the competition. Air-conditioning extracted from solar energy is now a very real capability to be offered by the well-organized solar energy company.

MORE SOLAR

The quintessential industrial application for solar energy may be the detoxification of hazardous chemicals. The Solar Energy Research Institute operates a pilot facility for this purpose in Golden, Colorado. Piped with a catalyst through transparent tubing centered in a parabolic solar collector, hard-to-dispose-of toxins like PCBs and dioxins are broken down molecularly by intense concentrated sunlight that can be magnified to 65,000 times the brightness of natural light. What's left is harmless water and carbon dioxide. A firm that latches on to this capability and enters into the business of effectively destroying man's hazardous waste will find a huge market ready, willing, and able to pay and an adoring public grateful for the initiative.

Solar power is proven in making ceramics, in metal refining, in irrigation pumps for remote farms, in water treatment in South America, and the grinding of grain in Asia. Successful solar energy experiments have produced hydrogen fuel from water. When burned, hydrogen simply regenerates water. Solar has been used routinely for decades to power spacecraft. Laser technology powered by the sun is being investigated. Wallboard impregnated with "phase change material" (PCMs) can be developed that stores solar energy by day for release at night. . . . All this, yet the market for solar is lightly tapped.

Seventy percent of South Africa is without electricity, ninety percent of India; more than half the world lives as before Thomas Edison. Ironically, these societies have the opportunity to leap beyond the First World in energy supplies if business will but bring them the solar products to do it. Solar energy is where mankind must soon draw its power. Developing nations are energy vacuums simply awaiting the delivery of solutions; it is not so simple for the industrialized world: we already have an energy system. A new one cannot simply be laid in on top of it—not very easily at least, and not without a tough fight from the guys who were there first.

The market for solar is there, the profit potential is there, the capital resources to launch and sustain well-positioned solar initiatives could be negotiated, the environmental pay-off is there—solar energy consumes only sunlight and gives off only energy. What's missing? The organizations to seize on the opportunity.

WIND POWER

There are other nonpolluting sources of energy that provide niches of opportunity for the business communi-ty. Commercially available wind machines have many of the stand-alone benefits of solar energy and can power most of the same applications, even at night when solar turns off. But wind machinery is limited to those environs where the wind blows regularly at thirteen mph or greater. Still, the potential of wind power is very significant. Tens of thou-sands of wind machines operate around the world today. More than 7,500 turbines turned by the wind generate electricity in Altamont Pass, California. The current is sold to Pacific Gas and Electric.

With more than two dozen states now requiring electric utilities to factor the costs of environmental degradation into their development plans, wind-power capacity in the United States is expected to triple by the end of the 1990s. It is estimated that all of America's electricity requirements could be supplied by wind turbines mounted on the windiest ten percent of the country, mostly ranches and agricultural land. Wind farms in the western United States have earned ranchers $30,000 per hectare (2.471 acres); raising cows on the same land generated $30 and accelerated the ground's demise with the grazing. As with solar, wind power's fullest potential may lie in miniaturized single-unit applications for the home or specific jobs like irrigation pumps. A firm that really took on the task of marketing and delivering wind energy systems to the whole range of possibilities could well capture a very substantial position in a substantial market.

Hydrothermal energy from the earth's interior generates electricity and heats water and living space in Italy, New Zealand, Idaho, Hawaii, and Iceland among other markets. This is exportable technology and know-how that gains wider market appreciation. Geothermal energy systems don't have to be tapped into a working volcano to be effective; many other areas of man's habitat can deliver commercial levels of this energy for those who know how to extract it and who have the organization to do it.

Only five percent of U.S. dams generate electricity. Ninety thousand megawatts of potential capacity exists, the equivalent of nearly 100 conventional coal-fired power plants. A firm organized to retrofit these structures with electricity-generating capacity should be able to turn a profit. Ocean thermal energy is a coming electricity-producing technology that draws energy from the temperature differences of sea water at the surface and at the depths. Coastal areas and island habitats could find this source of energy particularly attractive. Commercial plants are expected to be on-stream by the end of the century. The players in this field are already lining up for a piece of the action.

OTHER FUELS

The biggest part of research and development in alternate energy has to do with transportation fuels. It appears that there are no good short-term prospects for replacing gasoline, and there are those who realize that the supply is neither endless nor harmless. The U.S. Department of Energy, for one, is driving hard to come up with alternative liquid fuels in anticipation of the need. DOE and its various research and development partners in the oil and gas industry have some good candidates. Ethanol and methanol are clearly the front-runners. Ethanol, an alcohol brewed mostly from fermented corn, is currently the most widely used form of "renewable" liquid fuel. More than a billion gallons are blended with gasoline annually in the United States, up from just ten million gallons in 1979. Eight percent of all gasoline sold in the United States in 1988 had a ten percent blend of ethanol. Brazil and other South American countries rely *principally* on ethanol for transportation fuel. Methanol, made from biomass (plant life) or natural gas, appears to be the favorite gasoline alternative with DOE and the transportation industry. Natural gas in one form or another powers more than 30,000 vehicles in the United States Diesel fuel and gasoline are produced from biological material like trees, shrubs, seed crops, marine algae, and agricultural and municipal waste.

While each of these fuels has its pluses, all are flawed in

the way that conventional gasoline is flawed: to release their store of energy they must be exploded, combusted. Left over are waste emissions. Granted, there are important differences in the emissions. Living plants and the fuels derived from them have little sulfur content, a plus for the acid rain problem. Biologists think they can develop "fuel crops" low in nitrogen, another advantage in the fight against acid rain and greenhouse warming. Hydrocarbons, a major cause of ground-level pollution (smog) in Los Angeles and other big cities, are not a factor with biofuels, and carbon monoxide is reduced. Natural gas emits lower levels of nitrogen oxide and hydrocarbons than conventional gasoline. However, biofuels still release carbon dioxide, the principal cause of greenhouse warming, and other emissions like aldehydes, including formaldehyde. Some of this is potentially more dangerous than the waste presently streaming from the exhaust pipe. In actual use, natural gas proves to be only a little better in regard to hydrocarbon and nitrogen oxide emissions.

The alternative-fuel emission problem is compounded by a principle illustrated in the metals business. The aluminum industry has long touted the weight advantages of its product over steel. Aluminum is two-thirds the weight of steel, but it is also only about half as strong, so more aluminum is required to replace the same item in steel, reducing substantially the material's inherent weight advantage. The same is true with alternate fuel; it takes a lot more of it to get the same energy as conventional gasoline, so emission reductions are not as great as they appear on paper. A two-year trial run of ten United Parcel Service natural gas-powered delivery trucks in New York City expects to verify an anticipated reduction in nitrogen oxide emissions of twenty-five percent and a thirteen percent cut in hydrocarbons. Actual performance in methanol-powered buses in the same market found that lower levels of particulates and nitrogen oxides were emitted than in diesel buses but higher levels of hydrocarbons, carbon monoxide, and formaldehyde. "Reductions" on this scale will do little if anything about the global buildup of atmospheric pollutants. So when it is stated that natural gas or ethanol or some other biofuel doesn't pollute like conventional gasoline, understand that that doesn't mean there is no pollution; it is just a different kind of pollution. Simply transferring our gluttony for conventional gasoline to biofuels and natural gas is not a legitimate way out of the environmental noose in which we have stuck our collective necks. There's no gain in picking your poisons.

That said, alternative transportation fuels are coming; so are industrial biogases and pelletized solid fuels from organic scraps and waste. They do represent a substantially lesser poison than gasoline, oil, and coal. Renewable energy, including solar, contributed $18 billion of energy to mankind in 1990. Ten percent of all energy consumed in the United States is now renewable energy (most of it is wood, wood waste, and municipal waste, so the figure is a little deceiving). Ninety-two percent of the nation's total supply of accessible energy—resources that can be located, mined, and extracted using existing technology or technology available in the next three to five years—is renewable energy. Furthermore, renewable energy technology can be installed in units that are smaller and cheaper than conventional petroleum refineries, power plants, and other processes of energy production.

FUEL CROPS

The opportunities in alternative transportation and industrial fuels are those present in any major emerging industry. Products must be manufactured and distributed. Markets and consumer delivery systems must be developed. There are educational programs to be crafted, software to be designed, repairs and maintenance to be provided for, and pollution control equipment to be developed. One of the most promising opportunities is in the field of biofuel "crops."

With the technology to produce ethanol, methanol, gasoline, and diesel fuel from living plant life well established, and with new advances just on the horizon, the principal limiting factor in greater biofuel utilization is the available stock of raw material. It is poor business and bad morals to take huge swaths of corn crop from the mouths of hungry people to make fuels for automobiles. Equally as macabre is the prospect of chewing up large parts of earth's remaining forest cover to brew fuel. But scientists have developed promising "energy crops" that can be grown inexpensively on a grand scale ten times faster than normal trees and plants. Furthermore, some of these crops—herbaceous forage, grasses, and legumes—can be grown on marginal land that supports little life of any kind; and all plants absorb through the normal photosynthetic process the same amount of carbon dioxide that they release upon combustion. Burn a plant and its store of carbon is released as carbon dioxide; plant a replacement and the carbon dioxide is taken back and stored away as carbon. On paper, a cycle of harvesting and replanting energy crops should produce no net gain in carbon dioxide. The real world doesn't work "on paper"; still, the benefits of this approach to energy far exceed the present one.

Black locust, silver maple, sweet gum, sycamore, poplar, and eucalyptus tree species appear quite capable of meeting the energy crop goals set by the U.S. Solar Energy Research

Institute: ten dry tons per acre per year of material at costs of $2 per million British thermal units of energy produced. Herbaceous crops like perennial switchgrass and annual sorghums can meet or exceed the goal and can be planted and harvested with conventional farming equipment. Oilseed crops can be converted to a diesel fuel substitute. Rapeseed converts from oil to a diesel-like fuel in a one-step process and can be planted in the fall in southern climates, providing farmers an additional crop for the year. Microalgae have been developed to produce oils or lipids that can be processed to diesel oil. These microscopic plants thrive in salty ponds in desert environments and soak up large quantities of carbon dioxide as they grow—another fortuitous use of unproductive terrain. "Energy plantations," whether on traditional agricultural land, marginal land, or inhospitable desert, hold great promise for the environmental businessman. They could easily become the oil fields of the future.

Using a process called fast pyrolysis and equipment called a vortex reactor, the Solar Energy Research Institute and its partners in private industry have developed a system that converts plant material and organic waste to crude oil. The material can be used "as-is" as boiler fuel or processed into gasoline. A business venture built around this capability and extensive energy plantations could become an important crude oil supplier.

Fuelmaker Corporation, based in Vancouver, has introduced a home refueling system for natural gas-powered vehicles. The appliance will be sold through gas utilities, and already there is a backlog of orders for the initial units. There are other alternative fuels waiting effective means of delivery.

CHAPTER ELEVEN

FAST FORWARD

Business runs off capital. Capital, chasing profit and security, goes to the tried and proven and rarely to the start-up venture, the unproven market or the emerging industry. Environmental businesses with their unfamiliar terminologies and uncertainties are just the sort of ventures to bring apoplexy to your typical branch bank manager and venture capital group. When it comes to "bionomics," the economics of ecology, conventional financial institutions can be counted on to do what they have always done: follow developments and not lead; lend and invest when businesses are solid and profitable, not in the beginning when the money is most needed. The situation is no worse nor better for environmental businesses than it was for overnight parcel delivery "schemes" ten to twelve years ago or struggling computer firms before that. As with those early industries, the requisite financial infrastructure that will eventually undergird bionomics is only now beginning to crystallize; because everything about the environment is more pervasive and more pressing, the opportunities are commensurately larger today.

FINANCING

A score of investment funds have stepped forward to capitalize on environmental solutions of one kind or another, principally in the area of waste disposal. Oppenheimer's Global Environment Fund, Inc., launched in February 1990, will try to make money on garbage and toxic waste. The fund focuses on companies in pollution control, hazardous waste removal, and recycling. Hundreds of billions of dollars will be spent in the future to clean up toxic and nuclear waste, and Oppenheimer aims to get a piece of the action with its portfolio of companies. The much smaller New Alternatives Fund, operated by a father and son in New York, invests primarily in alternative energy companies. The $2 million SFT Environmental Awareness Fund was organized in 1988 in King of Prussia, Pennsylvania. The John Hancock insurance group invests in environmental solutions through its newly created Freedom Environment Fund. There are other funds organized in the belief that there's money to be made backing companies engaged in environmental work. The field is far from saturated. Investment funds targeted at solar energy, alternative transportation, "efficiency banking" (see below), or some other facet of the environmental problem would do just as well if not better than those now so narrowly focused.

At least two "environmental banks" have been organized in the United States, one in Connecticut and one in Colorado. Nothing facilitates corporate growth like a banking establishment that understands and covets your business. Environmental banks, organized and operated by bankers who know their way around the environmental arena, stand to gorge themselves on choice pickings while conventional lenders scratch their heads in confusion and disinterest. Conventional lenders and investors can be taught the economics of environmental enterprise, however. John Strode was able to show the conservative Atlanta-based C & S National Bank where the profit lay in solar energy panels. Strode's firm, Armech Solar Power, Inc., is constructing the world's largest photovoltaic solar panel manufacturing facility in a north Atlanta suburb. To the surprise of many, C & S is financing the project.

But not everyone can effectively communicate the earnings value of his or her environmental business. Entrepreneurs in the environmental arena are like entrepreneurs in any field, past or present. They are generally much better at the mystical feat of breathing life into a business venture than they are in dealing with the details required by bankers and investors. Comprehensive business plans have become a necessity in today's financial markets; nowhere is this need greater than when capitalizing unfamiliar environmental ventures. These business plans must be sophisticated enough to impress with management's grasp of the business but elementary enough to educate the lender or investor and "net out" the bottom line.

Corporate communications firms have long prepared annual reports and sophisticated financial presentations for clientele seeking to cultivate lasting financial relationships. This business, tailored to the specific needs of bionomics, would open up a large and growing market, particularly with an emphasis on business plans. The brilliant seat-of-the-pants Arkansas entrepreneur with a breakthrough invention in waste disposal has no chance of raising the $6 million needed to bring his product to market without a comprehensive, convincing business plan. For lack of this instrument, society slips backward in its climb out of environmental degradation.

Perhaps the best way to secure financing for a daring new environmental venture is to wrap the business in familiar clothing. Johnny Imerman of Mindis International (see "Recycling") built one of the largest and most advanced recycling businesses in the world by selling investors and lenders on the virtues of scrap metal. Financial types understand junkyards; recycling they are not so sure of. Another clever entrepreneur secured bank funding with contracts to haul restaurant slop. There was some surprise at the bank when it was learned that the borrower, a skilled engineer, was actually in the cosmetic soap business—rendered from the restaurant slop.

Working within the financial establishment has its limitations, however. Inevitably, new economic eras—bionomics is nothing less—require new financial institutions to advance the innovations of the day and a new economic philosophy to accommodate the changes. "Efficiency banks" in some shape or form fall in the first category, full-cost pricing in the latter.

"EFFICIENCY BANKS"

Throughout this book, reference is made to a variety of financial trade-offs for pollution reduction: emission reduction credit trading among industrial concerns for cash, carbon tax trading among nations for cash and like-kind goods and services, reduced electricity and water consumption swapped for a share of the utility savings realized ("Negawatts"), free-enterprise solutions to storm-water pollution, reduced automobile usage and traffic congestion in exchange for a slice of the money *not spent* to remedy the problems. These trade-offs and others founded in the same concept, all involving some form of efficiency, are very likely to evolve into powerful new financial institutions incorporating the disciplines of arbitrage, futures trading, commodity brokerage and banking. The catalyst necessary to bring this development to fruition has to be the right kind of banking institution, an "efficiency bank" that sees the cash profit in funding solutions to environmental degradation and knows where to look for its money.

A bright office-building owner should be able to drop in at the local efficiency bank and negotiate a deal to purchase super-efficient office equipment for his tenants and *give* the stuff to them in order to realize a greater economic gain from lower utility bills and savings in downsized electrical and mechanical systems (see "Efficiencies"). The bank would know to collect its loan and interest from the power company in small monthly add-ons to the borrower's substantially reduced electric bill. The utility may even pay part of the expense of the retrofit since it would be spared the cost of generating additional electricity to meet higher demand. A homeowner should be able to finance the purchase of a wastewater treatment appliance at the efficiency bank. Payback would come from the local water department, which, through the initiatives of the homeowner, gains treatment capacity at no cost and avoids the expense of adding that much new treatment capacity.

An efficiency bank could contribute substantially to improvements in urban congestion by financing the business of "remote employee services" (see "Real Estate"). Fund a complete employee "home office package," telecommunications equipment and systems, installation and all, and look to the employer for repayment. From savings realized in reduced office space requirements and related overhead, the employer should be well able to pay and still come out ahead on the transaction.

With a little imagination, the market for efficiency banks is boundless. Who would go after the business?

CARBON TAX TRADING

The ascendancy of full-cost-pricing economics has begun, creating new waves of opportunities in accounting, auditing, financial analyses, economic forecasting, and economic indices (see "Indices"). Carbon tax trading among nations to curb global pollution becomes more and more feasible with the emergence of full-cost pricing. Like emission reduction credits, carbon taxes would involve a trade-off of pollution reduction for cash or like-kind goods or services. A global standard would be set for a given pollutant, say carbon dioxide. Every nation that reduced emissions below the standard would earn credits that could be sold to countries that exceed the standard. The noncomplying countries could pay in hard currency and/or projects like schools, hospitals, sewer systems, and so on. Third World countries with little industrial base are the best candidates to earn reduction credits. A worldwide carbon tax system could prove the ways and means of raising their standards of living while eliminating the need to strip important global habitat just to survive. Industrial nations like the United States would have to pay for their right to pollute above the global standard, putting them at a competitive disadvantage against more efficient (less polluting) industrial complexes like those of the Japanese. Eventually, the *purchasers* of pollution credits would have to become more efficient to keep costs in line.

It's an exciting prospect and a real opportunity for "market-makers." Market-makers are particularly important at this early stage in the evolution of environmental enterprise. The fledgling emission reduction credit trading business, including carbon tax development and practices in negawatt trade-offs, is being shaped right now by a handful of pioneers who could be sitting at the top of an illustrious industry ten to fifteen years from now. Newfound commodities from man's virulent waste-stream need brokers and traders to develop after-markets and close the recycling loop. Those market-makers first in ride the wave the highest.

Franchising needs to come round to bionomics in a big way. It is an excellent vehicle for putting ready-to-go, "packaged" businesses into the marketplace in a hurry. And sound environmental solutions need to be implemented in a hurry. Just Bulbs, Just Water, "environmental car dealerships"—these franchise ideas noted earlier are but a few of the possibilities. Backing franchise operations that sell well-conceived turnkey environmental businesses would be good business for efficiency banks or investment funds. Insurance is one of the hottest topics in the environmental arena. Superfund legislation created tremendous liabilities for polluters; unexpected dangers from pell-mell industrial growth seem to be under every rock. Insurers don't know what to insure, how long to insure it, or how much premium to charge to make money on the service. Tremendous opportunities exist in this tumultuous new field of environmental insurance.

Nothing of any consequence is going to happen in environmental enterprise without huge infusions of capital. As goes one, goes the other.

POPULATION MANAGEMENT

Human overpopulation is too lethal a problem to be controversial, too urgent to get so little attention, too complex to be left to governments alone to solve. By any measure, human habitat—not the big wide world, just that small part on which man can live—is behind the population power-curve. Very literally, mankind today steals the vital planetary resources of its progeny to maintain the lifestyle to which it has become accustomed. Perhaps nowhere is the population problem worse than in the United States, points out renowned population expert Dr. Paul Ehrlich of Stanford University. "The United States . . . has a gigantic population. We're the fourth-largest nation; we have over a quarter of a billion people. Our affluence, our consumption level, is incredible because we specialize in a pattern of planned obsolescence. . . . What it boils down to is that the birth of an average American baby is something like twenty to one hundred times the disaster for the planet's life-support systems as the birth of a baby in Bangladesh or Kenya or India."

One way or the other, human population will crash—soon, in the opinion of some leading experts. In the most optimistic confluence of cooperative actions, the community of man could rein in its numbers precipitously. In the absence of such a commitment, the laws of nature will do the job for us. Under the weight of current *net* population additions—95 million annually—the carrying capacity of human habitat will fail, and populations will fall to whatever levels can be sustained by the habitat remaining. Population control will have occurred. The toll will be appalling. Residents of the United States and other prosperous societies are no more immune to the laws of nature than any other people or species. The only uncertainty with overpopulation is where the breaking point is. Dr. Ehrlich illustrates the danger with an analogy to the exponential growth of a pond weed. "If you introduce a pond weed, and you know that it will double the amount of pond it covers every day, and that it will cover the pond in thirty days, the question is: How much of the pond will be covered in twenty-nine days? And the answer is, just half; so it's the last day when everything goes to pot. Similarly, our population growth and the patterns in which we've depleted various resources and launched our assault on the planet's life-support system are roughly exponential."

Solutions? The only one that has worked besides wholesale annihilation and the "natural corrective procedure" is contraception within the context of well-delivered family planning services. Sterilization policies, voluntary or otherwise, have failed in China, India, Brazil, and other countries that have every incentive for them to work. Abortion sports the same track record. Family planning and related contraceptive health services are proven effective, but, contrary to popular belief, they are not widely available. Therese Locoh, director of research for the French Center for Population and Development, notes what is well known among demographers and family planning workers: "When it comes to distributing pills and contraceptives, few countries have truly effective programs. What is most serious is that the demand for family planning that exists is not being met."

Is there a market here for free-enterprise, profit-motivated solutions to human overpopulation? There is certainly a bountiful supply of *users* for effective population management products and services. To reduce the world's average family size from its current level of almost four children per woman to 3.2 by the year 2000, the United Nations Population Fund (UNPF) estimates that 350 million couples will have to be sold on family planning programs. Nine billion dollars is projected for the various UNPF programs. Those are the figures of a major market. The expertise, programs, contraceptive devices, medical services, and other tools of the trade are available. The need for effective, humane solutions is great, and the political will probably exists to provide access to markets, were they to be identified.

But how do you get paid? That's the big question. Those who need the products and services of population management, for the most part, cannot pay. Nevertheless, tremendous financial resources are expended by governments, rich and poor, and international relief organizations in the name of population contro,l and even more money is spent coping with the results of overpopulation: feeding and "watering" more and more people, providing more and more shelter and energy and health care and sanitary services, and on and on, more and more. The expenses are real. Money is being spent; it's available. It is just not buying much. Perhaps by borrowing a page from the new book of pollution reduction trading (see "Financing"), the business community can find a way to get paid for swinging its great resources into the problem of overpopulation.

Companies organized to profit from the business of population management would first have to illustrate where the present collective *cost*, direct and indirect, of overpopulation far exceeds the *price* of purchasing effective family planning and contraceptive services. In the Third World, family planning can be delivered for an average of just $16 per couple per year. Oral contraceptives can cost as little as $2 per year. Armed with good full-cost-pricing data and comprehensive business plans for delivering their services, population management firms may be able to trade off population reductions for a portion of the money *not spent* to deal with the problem. The savings would accrue to the governments at risk and to the world community at large via its various health and relief organizations. Negotiate the mechanics for paying the bills from *saved money*, and the necessary components of a market-driven solution to overpopulation are in place.

Now let's consider the shape and substance of population management firms: what services must they provide to be effective? The task, of course, is to reduce population growth; that is more than a function of family planning and contraception, however. Where possible, stresses need to be taken off tottering habitat so that it can carry more of the people who rely on it. This may mean the introduction of stand-alone alternative energy devices like photovoltaic units, thermal solar panels, or wind machines to eliminate the need to strip needed forestlands for fuel. The labor freed up from *not having* to forage for fuel can be put to more productive uses. Low-cost water treatment and conservation measures could provide more usable water and reduce disease, a major drain on the productive resources of Third World populaces. There is the possibility of relocating populations from habitat that cannot support them to ones that can. Like exhausted farmland allowed to go fallow, the vacated habitat might then be nursed back to health via actions taken by the population management organization—resurfacing depleted farmland with industrial compost, reforestation, replenishing water resources, installing energy systems, and so on. The Third World incentive to have many children for old-age security could be removed with some kind of rudimentary social security program designed and initiated by the "company" and funded by a consortium of the host government and world relief organizations. Good prenatal health care has proven to take away the incentive in many societies to have large families to compensate for high infant mortality rates.

So a population management firm must bring an array of capabilities to the table, nothing farfetched or exotic, just an uncommon alliance of skills: conventional family planning and contraceptive services delivered with all the marketing skills, logistical wherewithal, and cost-effectiveness that only free-enterprise capitalism can muster; demographic computer models and databases to calculate the carrying capacity of human habitat; technical know-how to recognize where and how habitat can be enhanced and the operational apparatus to implement programs that make sense; actuarial and pension fund expertise. . . . Who would make a market in this business of population management?

LAW

The environmental law business did not exist in the 1970s; today it is the fastest-growing segment of the legal profession. The "hottest" area of environmental law currently is in land transactions. The concern for liability has become so intense that "you can't borrow money on a piece of property or sell it to any sort of real estate investor without having it investigated environmentally," notes a leading environmental lawyer. What's hot will change, however. Lawyers will shape the new economics of environmentalism and prepare the way for the advancement of various industries. They will draw up the paperwork, draft the legislation, fight the legal battles, and convert philosophy into law.

The issue of privatization versus public ownership looms large in the future of environmental enterprise. Can private business do a better job of safeguarding man's habitat than government? The answer in many cases is certainly yes. The U.S. government, after all, "owned" the great bison herds of the old West and was responsible for their care. Had they been owned by ranching interests of the day or Indian tribal councils, perhaps their economic value would have saved them from near extinction. The elephant herds of Zimbabwe flourish under for-profit tourism and management practices administered by quasi-private tribal councils that "own" the animals; the publicly owned elephants of Kenya perish with alarming rapidity. If the great Grand Banks fishing grounds off Newfoundland were owned by private business, might they be better managed and preserved to the benefit of all of us? Might an entertainment organization like Walt Disney do more for the preservation of natural places than the U.S. Bureau of Land Management with its mixed mandate to preserve and protect . . . and log and mine and graze and drill.

Is this to say that government should turn over man's habitat to the private sector to manage and control? Certainly not. The best of both public and private capabilities must be incorporated into a body of law that maximizes the carrying capacity of man's remaining habitat. This is vital work for the legal profession. The legal mechanics of special tax districts need to be honed so that the business of alternative transportation can take root. The implementation of green fees, pollution taxes and other penalties and incentives needs to be accelerated to both inhibit environmentally degrading practices and fund the transition to the new economy. There is much new and inventive work here to be done.

As with the advertising and public relations industry (see "Communications"), the successful environmental law practice will take on new dimensions for the job ahead. Environmental law is going to have to be "sold," sold to the public, sold to legislators, sold to business. There is not the normal evolutionary time frame for events to pull the law in their wake. The law must keep abreast of the advent of environmental solutions and, when initiatives lag, even take the lead in opening the way for developments to materialize. The environmental law firm with polished communication and marketing capabilities will prevail over the competition without them. Because so much of environmentalism is steeped in technology, biology, physics, and other sciences, the wise environmental law firm will possess the expertise to navigate in these waters. Capital formation is critical to environmental enterprise; the law firm with the financial acumen to advise and innovate in these matters would be valuable indeed.

NATURE MANAGEMENT

Johnny Appleseed planted trees as his avocation and vocation. The concept, refined and practiced on a worldwide scale, has legitimate commercial possibilities today. In concert with the oceans, trees are the mechanism that keeps atmospheric carbon dioxide in balance. But because the total of global forest coverage is greatly diminished, because current annual consumption of wood exceeds regrowth by fifty percent, carbon dioxide is out of balance. It accumulates in the atmosphere and the earth warms up and no one knows where it will stop. Plant a tree and it soaks up carbon dioxide and holds it as carbon so long as the wood is not burned or allowed to decay. Plant enough trees and greenhouse warming *could* be checked. It would take a nearly impossible *net* addition of trees to do the job—coverage the size of the United States—but a big company or companies, planting every nook and cranny of man's habitat, paid by host governments and the world community, all of which would benefit from the service, could make a go of the reforestation business.

How about companies to refurbish and reclaim degraded habitat—cleaning up waste disposal sites, resurfacing depleted soils with industrial compost, cleansing water supplies, reestablishing natural drainage systems, replanting trees and other ground cover, and so on.

Who would capitalize on forestlands without tearing them down? Certain crops can be grown in the midst of forests, producing cash revenue *and* preserving critical habitat for man and animal. Medicines can be extracted from plants and trees without destroying the forest. Might theme park operators develop from forests and other natural places profitable "environmental theme parks" featuring nature walks, wildlife preserves, outdoor concerts, and rustic conference facilities?

Eco-tourism is catching on. Prosperous vacationers spend big bucks to go to Australia to live for ten days with the aborigines, for example. An appreciation is gained for the lifestyle and the things necessary to sustain it, like space and undisturbed natural food supplies; and the aborigines make a little money for their part in the enterprise. Expand on the trend in eco-tourism with "primitive hunting" packages that feature big-game hunting the old-fashioned way—with spear and shield, primitive bow and arrow. Spend a week or two getting the basics down with the Walbiri, Masai, the Inuit, the Punan, or the Sioux; then go out on foot after the quarry. Get up-close and personal with the lion, leopard, bison, elk, or bear. Any trophies bagged on these safaris would be well earned, and a great deal more wildlife would live to die of old age.

ET CETERA

The emergence of environmentalism has created a field day for consultants of every description. Neither business nor government has developed the in-house expertise to deal with unfolding environmental issues. Guidance and support must come from "outside consultants." Demand is high and going up, the supply of real environmental expertise is small yet ill-defined and slow to recognize its marketability—fertile ground indeed for the entrepreneur. Job placement, executive search, and employee training services tailored to the environmental marketplace should be welcomed with open arms. Someone has to install, maintain, and repair the alternative energy and transportation systems that come on-stream. Managers must be acquired or trained who can thread their way through growing regulatory guidelines. Skilled environmental executives will be needed to launch new enterprises. . . .

There is probably money to be made in establishing a permanent pipeline to expeditiously transfer stocks of food and water from places of surplus to places of deficit. International food relief organizations react to crises on a catch-as-catch-can basis. The apparatus of response and delivery is not a thing of permanence; hunger and starvation are. Why not set up now for the business at hand?

"Planetary managers" might get into things like painting Phoenix white to cut down heat absorption and the fossil fuel emissions necessary to keep people cool in 120-degree temperatures, or "salting" the oceans with hundreds of thousands of tons of iron ore to offset greenhouse warming. Vast stretches of marine algae would result, sucking from the atmosphere the excess carbon dioxide, it is said.

There are tracers, odorants, coloring agents, isotopes, and other markers to track sources of pollution to build a business around. Rising sea levels expected from greenhouse warming will flood large coastal areas. The diking technology and expertise developed in the Netherlands might be assimilated now for export to those places that will need it. There must be a market for coastal maps that illustrate the projected rise in water and the land losses that will result. Many hard economic decisions will be made on this information. Want not for the stuff of environmental enterprise. It's a realm of unprecedented opportunity. Environmental sensitivities have opened up the entire spectrum of the marketplace to "green" products, services, and lifestyles. At present, the charlatans mingle freely with the purists, but the timing has never been better to correct past production, consumption, and disposal practices. The consumer will grow to distinguish the ruse from the real thing. Come forth now with the parts and fabric of the new environmental economy; push the market for the good of us all. Bring on the alternative transportation and energy forms, the substitutes for toxins and corrosives, the popular programming to educate and prepare us, the efficiency and recycling measures, the penalties and incentives to facilitate the transition, the new living and working environments, the fashion of more pedestrian lifestyles. . . . The market is ready. It must be ready.

If fifty years from now today's babies and their fellows in the family of man are not caught in a terrifying, painfully evident plunge into oblivion it will be because a new breed of businessman and consumer achieved dominance in the world economic order in the 1990s. If, fifty years from now, the environmental problem is in check and mankind faces the prospect of a healthy, nurturing habitat far into the future, few will recognize that a bullet was dodged, one fired from way in the past by unwitting forebears shooting in the dark.